20th CENTURY
TRIVIA
Quizbook

20th CENTURY
TRIVIA
Quizbook

Compiled by

Fid Backhouse & Richard Widdows

Illustrations by Mike Webb

BROCKHAMPTON
PRESS

CONTENTS

Continued overleaf ➤ ➤ ➤ ➤ ➤ ➤ ➤ ➤ ➤ ➤

CONTENTS

ANSWERS START ON PAGE 204

Beat Knowall at his own game (with a little help from Bonzo)

I'M PRETTY HOT !!!

BUT NOT AS HOT AS ME.

Knowall thinks he's brilliant, but unfortunately he always gets his answers wrong. Enjoy beating him at his own game by answering Knowall's questions correctly . . . with a little help from Bonzo, who'll always give you a clue to the right answer.

QUIZ NUMBER I

Knowall's question:

Which fictional character has been portrayed most often in films?

FATHER CHRISTMAS !!!

1 In education, what do the letters GCSE represent?

2 The won is the currency of which two Asian countries?

3 What is the Princess Royal's first name?

4 Which daily cartoon strip is drawn by Maurice Dodd?

5 What was the world's first antibiotic, available in 1941?

6 By which name is the cachalot also known?

7 In what year did the Spanish Civil War end?

8 Legally speaking, what does JP stand for?

9 How is myopia commonly described?

10 Which designer introduced the "New Look" in 1947?

11 In what year did *Breakfast TV* begin?

12 What was the profession of Frank Lloyd Wright?

13 Of which US state is Helena the capital?

14 In 1996, which former Gladiator sued LWT?

15 What replaced Britain's profits tax in 1966?

16 In the Commons, which MP is entitled to be called "the Father of the House"?

17 Which moving film starring John Hurt was based on the life of John Merrick?

18 Which video cassette system, introduced in the 1970s, failed to compete with VHS and disappeared?

19 To what was Tony Blair referring when he said: "There isn't a more famous English pub."?

20 Which year marked the centenary of the first car death on British roads: 1976, 1981, 1986, 1991, 1996?

21 What is the surname of the gamekeeper in D.H. Lawrence's novel *Lady Chatterley's Lover*?

22 In 1902 which two figures, later famous in Russia, first met at 30 Holford Square, King's Cross, London?

23 Who crashed at 328mph (528km/h) on Coniston Water in 1967 attempting to raise his world speed record?

24 In 1994, what notorious international killer was finally arrested in Khartoum after years of pursuit?

25 Which erudite television presenter was dubbed "the thinking man's crumpet" by Frank Muir?

26 The "Electraglide" is a classic make of motor-bike produced by which company?

27 How many of the world's countries are "landlocked" (have no coastline): 16, 26, 36, 46, 56, 66?

28 What natural red dye is produced from the dried bodies of Mexican insects?

29 Who was Anne Mansfield Sullivan's famous deaf, dumb and blind pupil?

30 What were both Lt-Col Herbert Jones and Sgt Ian John McKay awarded in 1992?

AN ELEMENTARY MISTAKE, MY DEAR KNOWALL.

Answers on page 204

Knowall's question:

What is the capital of the state of Illinois?

CHICAGO !!!

1 In computer terms, what is ROM?

2 What do the initials D.C. stand for after Washington?

3 In what sport is the Calcutta Cup a trophy?

4 What colour is a New York taxi?

5 In 1971, who retired to Colombey-les-Deux-Eglises?

6 Who perfected the first ball-point pen in 1938?

7 What was the name of the butler in *The Addams Family*?

8 Which Irishman won both a Nobel Prize and an Oscar?

9 How did the supermarket chain Tesco get its name?

10 Which Hollywood star was Carrie Fisher's mother?

11 What American city is "the beer capital of the world"?

12 Where did The Police go walking in 1979?

13 What breed of dog is Scooby Doo?

14 Who has a villa at Castel Gandolfo?

15 Which cricket commentator was called "Jonners"?

16 Which item of dress was introduced by the fashion entrepreneur Mr Fish in the late 1960s?

17 Which commercial radio station broadcast on 208 metres in the medium wave?

18 To what drink does the French phrase *eau de vie* usually refer?

19 What is the design style of the 1920s and 1930s using geometric shapes and bright metal finishes?

20 Which island nation, formerly a British colony, has Sinhalese and Tamil as its two official languages?

21 Before the creation of British Airways, what did the initials B.O.A.C. stand for?

22 Which English city's modern cathedral has a glass cylinder with 16 pinnacles forming a crown of thorns?

23 In 1995 which country overtook the USA and France as the biggest supplier of arms to the Third World?

24 Which author, better known for his spy thrillers, wrote *Chitty Chitty Bang Bang*?

25 What major new town has been developed since 1967 in Buckinghamshire?

26 Name the paedophile who led police to gruesome discoveries in Belgium in 1996.

27 Britain had only one colony on the South American mainland. What was it?

28 Which Essex constituency did Winston Churchill represent in the Commons from 1945 to 1964?

29 Name one of the two Football League clubs for which Brian Clough played.

30 Who is the "'arry" referred to in a string of predictable responses from heavyweight champion Frank Bruno?

HE'S NO SPRING CHICKEN.

Answers on page 204

QUIZ NUMBER 3

Knowall's question:

Where, exactly, did Charles propose to Diana?

ON THE THRONE !!!

1 Which chain store was founded by Selim Zilkha in 1961: Argos, Body Shop, Habitat, Mothercare, Next?

2 Which New Zealand artist reached No. 4 in the singles charts in 1991 with *World in Union*?

3 What is the name of the Ivy League university situated in Cambridge, Massachusetts?

4 Name the footballer who captained England's World Cup winning team in 1966.

5 In which 1972 disaster movie was a luxury ocean liner engulfed by a tidal wave?

6 Who beat Sebastian Coe to take the gold medal in the 800 metres at the 1980 Olympics in Moscow?

7 The character Basildon Bond was created by which television comedian?

8 Which Indiana city consistently registered the highest US murder rate in the early 1990s?

9 What musical device first appeared as the "John Gabel Entertainer" in California in 1906?

10 In the film *Who Framed Roger Rabbit?*, what was the name of poor Roger's sensational wife?

11 Why did 13-year-old Jordy Schwarz hit the news headlines in August 1993?

12 What was the name of the gravel-voiced chauffeur in the television series *Hart to Hart*?

13 Vanessa and Lynn Redgrave are the daughters of which knighted actor?

14 What world "first" for youngsters was held at Crystal Palace on 4 September 1909?

15 Which foreign king married – and divorced – an English girl called Toni Gardiner?

16 In what year did women first compete In the Olympic athletics: 1904, 1908, 1912, 1920, 1924, 1928?

17 John Thaw and Dennis Waterman played the lead roles in which pioneering 1970s TV police series?

18 Who shared Terry Waite's imprisonment by terrorists in Lebanon and was released at the same time?

19 In which year were pubs allowed to open all day on Sundays: 1988, 1989, 1990, 1991 or 1992?

20 Which 1993 film took a monster $81.7 million in its first week in American cinemas?

21 The 1986 battles between Rupert Murdoch and the printing unions occurred in which area of London?

22 In what year did Gazza blub after losing to the Germans and Maggie blub after losing office?

23 Britain's first colour supplement appeared with which newspaper in 1962?

24 What is the approximate frequency of twins in Britain: one In 20, 40, 60, 80 or 100 births?

25 The grandson of which powerful foreign leader started at Millfield School, Somerset in 1996?

26 What do these have in common: *Tevye the Milkman, I Am a Camera, Pygmalion, Liliom, The Matchmaker*?

27 If Neil Kinnock had won the 1992 general election, who would have become deputy prime minister?

28 Who was arrested for prostitution at the MGM Hotel in Las Vegas, Nevada in September 1996?

29 Which television and film character is associated with the line "Live long and prosper"?

30 Which composer was the first musician to receive a life peerage – in the year he died, 1976?

BETTER THAN TALKING TO PLANTS.

Answers on page 204

Knowall's question:

Which Poet Laureate was appointed as Australia's Governor-General in 1902?

JOHN MASEFIELD !!!

1 Before he abandoned his career for painting, what was French artist Paul Gauguin's profession?

2 In 1909, what ship did Captain Robert Scott acquire for a forthcoming Antarctic expedition?

3 The woman known as the "Grandmother of Europe" died in 1901. Who was she?

4 In 1909, what store with the slogan "all your shopping under one roof" opened in Oxford Street?

5 Which country's navy annihilated the Russian Baltic Fleet in a fierce battle of 1905?

6 The lives of travelling New Yorkers would never be the same after 27 October 1904. Why?

7 Which organisation that today claims to be the "fourth emergency service" was founded in June 1905?

8 Two new states were admitted to the United States of America in 1905. Name one of them.

9 Which French writer who died in 1902 was known for championing individual and social underdogs?

10 Which American president put the US Army in charge of building the Panama Canal?

11 A dam was finally completed in 1902 to transform a nation's economy. Which nation and what dam?

12 In September 1901, which prominent American figure did anarchist Leon Czolgosz assassinate?

13 Over which German-Swiss lake did the world's first rigid-frame airship LZ1 make its maiden flight?

14 What revolutionary scientific theory did Max Planck put forward in 1900?

15 Which important Cretan site did British archaeologist Arthur Evans excavate in the early 1900s?

16 The Nobel Prize for Chemistry was awarded to which British scientist in 1908 for his work on radioactivity?

17 In the 1900s, what fearsome naval weapon sparked off an arms race between Britain and Germany?

18 Who went camping for the first time in 1907, choosing Brownsea Island in Poole Harbour for the experiment?

19 What was the name of the murderous Indian cult who worshipped Kali and were still active in this decade?

20 Which significant announcement regarding the US dollar was made in March 1900?

21 What was the first name of French aviator Blériot who was first to fly the English Channel in 1909?

22 Which London stadium was built for the 1908 Olympic Games and opened with a Franco-British exhibition?

23 The phrase "conditioned reflexes" was coined after experiments with dogs in 1907. By whom?

24 Where in the Hawaiian Islands did President Taft authorise the building of a new naval base in 1909?

25 Name the well-known campaigner who founded the militant wing of the Women's Suffrage Movement.

26 In 1906, the Italian town of Ottaiano was overwhelmed by the eruption of which volcano?

27 Which Russian battleship became notorious when the crew mutinied at Odessa in 1905?

28 Name the South African "civil rights" leader released from prison by General Smuts in 1908.

29 Which famous Russian playwright died shortly after the premier of his work *The Cherry Orchard* in 1904?

30 What drug developed in Germany and still widely used today first went on sale in 1905?

ANYONE FOR TENNIS?

Answers on page 204

QUIZ NUMBER 5

Knowall's question:

In 1915, who built the first all-metal aeroplane in Germany?

MESSERSCHMITT !!!

1 Where was the 1915 Derby run after the Epsom racecourse was requisitioned by the army?

2 Swiss philanthropist Jean-Henri Dunant died in 1910. What international organisation did he found?

3 Name any two of the four film personalities who founded United Artists in 1919.

4 What did the House of Lords reluctantly surrender in August 1911?

5 In which London street were three anarchists burned to death in a house after a 1910 gun battle and siege?

6 Which Polish Communist was murdered following her arrest in the failed "Spartacist" rising in Berlin in 1919?

7 What did British airmen Hawker and Grieve fail to do in May 1919?

8 Who appeared on a famous 1914 recruiting poster pointing his finger and saying he "wants YOU"?

9 In 1919, where was the German fleet scuttled by its disgruntled crew members?

10 What London exhibition centre became an emergency internment camp for enemy "spies" in 1914?

11 The world's largest railway station opened in New York City in February 1913. What is it called?

12 In April 1912, which innovative new military corps was set up in Britain?

13 Which two parties tied with 272 seats each in the 1910 British general election?

14 What was the profession of Benito Mussolini, who founded Italy's fascist party in 1919?

15 Who was appointed as First Lord of the Admiralty in October 1911?

16 A suffragette bomb was found in which great London church in 1913?

17 After what town was Germany's new republic named, following World War 1?

18 What famous car mascot was commissioned by Rolls-Royce in 1911?

19 Which country demanded South Tyrol, Trieste and Istria as the price of staying neutral in World War 1?

20 What famous comedy policemen made their film debut in September 1912?

21 In what year did women win their long struggle to vote in a British general election?

22 After decades in power, which Mexican dictator finally fell in May 1911?

23 Name one of two popular dances banned for the members of German forces by the Kaiser in 1913.

24 The first shots of World War 1 were exchanged by which two countries on 1 August 1914?

25 Which French province lost in 1871 was reclaimed from Germany in 1918?

26 Which two Bolshevik leaders seized power in Russia in November 1917?

27 Which Irish leader defended northern loyalist interests during the Home Rule debate?

28 What was the name of the 1916 rebellion in Ireland which led to over 1,300 casualties?

29 What did Sir Arthur Lee give to the nation in 1917 for perpetual use by the British prime minister?

30 In 1912, which anaesthetic drug was condemned by an American doctor as likely to create "a race of fiends"?

I BET IT WAS A LOAD OF OLD JUNK.

Answers on page 205

QUIZ NUMBER 6

Knowall's question:

In 1925, Tennessee biology teacher John Scopes was fined $100 for telling pupils about what?

SEX ???

1 Who was voted president of the National Socialist German Workers' Party in July 1921?

2 On what day of the week did the famous Wall Street Crash of 1929 take place?

3 In August 1920, the 19th Amendment to the US Constitution granted what privilege to women?

4 What two innovative British currency items were issued for the first time in November 1928?

5 In 1921, what did the victorious Allies set at £10 billion to be paid off over 42 years?

6 Name the world's then-largest airship, which made its maiden passenger voyage over London in 1929.

7 What came into existence in 1922 when the Dail Eirann approved a treaty with Britain?

8 After 14 years, England regained what from Australia in August 1926?

9 Who, with two male companions in 1928, was the first woman to fly the Atlantic?

10 Which great "Man of Destiny" died in Moscow on 21 January 1924?

11 Soon to become a familiar sight all over Britain, what first appeared in London on 2 December 1929?

12 Which royal competed in the men's doubles at the "Golden Jubilee" Wimbledon in 1926?

13 What did the American Academy of Motion Picture Arts and Sciences introduce in 1929?

14 Which famous polar explorer died in a plane crash while searching for a missing Italian airship?

15 In reiterating the Balfour Declaration in 1921, what did Winston Churchill promise the Jewish people?

16. In 1928 how muoh was the first old age penslon paid in Britain: 5/- (25p), 10/- (50p), £1, £2, £2/10s (£2.50)?

17. What defeated empire signed a peace deal with the Allies in 1920 which reduced its size by 80%?

18. The widow of Edward VII died in December 1925. What was her name?

19. What character by Belgian cartoonist Hergé appeared for the first time in January 1929?

20. To which international organisation was Germany admitted in 1926?

21. In 1927, who set a new world land speed record at 174mph (280km/h) in *Bluebird*?

22. What new medical service was started in 1928 to serve the people of Australia's outback?

23. What did Abdul Aziz ibn Saud rename his country after being crowned King of the Hejaz at Mecca in 1926?

24. In 1923, how much did a loaf cost in Germany: 5,000, 250,000, 10 million, 500 million or 200 billion marks?

25. Name the aircraft in which Charles Lindbergh made the first solo Atlantic crossing from New York to Paris.

26. Which new dance that scandalised America took Britain by storm in 1925?

27. What name was adopted officially by the new kingdom of Serbs, Croats and Slovenes in 1929?

28. The Swallow Sidecar Company was founded in the 1920s. What famous car marque did it become?

29. What limit did the US Senate put on annual immigration in 1921: 51,295, 117,581, 283,101, 355,461, 500,000?

30. What was seen in Britain for the first time in over 200 years on 29 June 1927?

THAT'S A POOR SELECTION.

Answers on page 205

Knowall's question:

Which dynamic press baron launched the new United Empire Party in 1930?

LORD NORTHCLIFFE !!!

1 On what date in 1939 did Britain officially declare war on Germany?

2 In 1936, from which northern town did a famous unemployment march set off for London?

3 Which prominent public figure was granted German citizenship on 25 February 1932?

4 Name the Abyssinian emperor whose country was invaded by Italy in 1935.

5 In what river was the German battleship *Graf Spee* scuttled by its crew in December 1939?

6 Name the England and Surrey cricketer who retired in 1935 after scoring 197 first-class centuries.

7 Who beat Adolf Hitler in Germany's 1932 presidential election after calling him "that Austrian corporal"?

8 Which country left the League of Nations in 1933 after being censured for invading Manchuria?

9 What was the popular name of the alliance between Italy and Germany signed in 1939?

10 Britain's most prolific author of the day with 130 "shockers" to his credit died in 1932. Who was he?

11 In 1930, French troops left the German region they had occupied since World War 1. What was it?

12 Who explained that he could not discharge his duties "without the help and support of the woman I love"?

13 Name the enigmatic British hero who died after a Dorset motorcycle crash in 1935.

14 Which bitterly fought three-year European civil war broke out in July 1936?

15 In June 1939, what major event did George VI and Queen Elizabeth attend in New York?

16 In Spain, what Basque town was badly damaged by German bombers in 1937?

17 What European country did Italian troops invade in April 1939?

18 Which new British airport was planned in 1935 to relieve air traffic congestion?

19 Who was sentenced to death in 1935 for kidnapping and murdering aviator Charles Lindbergh's baby son?

20 In 1937, which hugely successful American popular composer died of a brain tumour aged 38?

21 Which dashing Spanish soldier and transatlantic air-man led a failed Republican coup attempt in 1930?

22 What did Franklin D. Roosevelt promise the American people if they elected him president in 1932?

23 In 1934, which dictator watched as his country won the first soccer World Cup held in Europe?

24 Which mild-mannered former chicken farmer headed Germany's concentration camp programme from 1934?

25 Who was the charismatic leader of the British Union of Fascists in the 1930s?

26 Which British battleship was sunk in Scapa Flow by a German sub in the first weeks of World War 2?

27 England's "greatest contemporary composer" died in 1934. Who was he?

28 Who became British prime minister in 1935 after Ramsay MacDonald resigned through ill-health?

29 In August 1939, which two European dictators declared they would never go to war against each other?

30 Which new Buckinghamshire film studio was opened by J. Arthur Rank in 1936?

KEEP BEAVERING AWAY AND YOU'LL GET THERE.

Answers on page 205

QUIZ NUMBER 8

Knowall's question:

Who gave a V-sign to the US Congress in 1941?

ADOLF HITLER !!!

1 In 1947, which president of the Screen Actors' Guild warned against a Communist witch-hunt in Hollywood?

2 What new form of housing appeared in 1944, having a living room, two bedrooms, bathroom and kitchen?

3 In the early weeks of 1940, which small nation gallantly resisted advancing Russian troops in the Winter War?

4 Who became the new leader of Argentina in 1945 with support from "The Shirtless Ones"?

5 Which rebel daughter of Lord Redesdale was sent back to Britain by Hitler in 1940 after a suicide bid?

6 Why did British Chancellor of the Exchequer Hugh Dalton resign in 1947?

7 Which prominent Nazi flew to Scotland in 1941 with a message for the Duke of Hamilton?

8 What Charlie Chaplin film satirising the dangers of Hitler didn't actually open in London until 1940?

9 Including civilians, how many people are thought to have died in World War 2: 25, 35, 45, 55 or 65 million?

10 In 1942, what Czech village was destroyed with its people in reprisal for the killing of Reinhard Heydrich?

11 Which long-serving Prime Minister of Ireland was voted out of office in 1948 after 16 years?

12 What was the actual date of V-E Day, which marked the official end of World War 2 in Europe?

13 Where, in 1943, did the first mass Allied landings in Europe take place?

14 In which Scottish city was an enduring arts festival established in 1947?

15 By what means did the Western Allies defeat Russia's blockage of Berlin in 1948 and 1949?

16 What 1949 Ealing comedy featured Scottish islanders looting a ship laden with Scotch?

17 Where did British rule end at midnight on 14 August 1947 with the blowing of a conch shell?

18 How did American General George "Blood and Guts" Patton die in 1945?

19 Which Chinese Nationalist leader was finally defeated by Mao Tse-tung's Communists in 1949?

20 At which British football ground were 33 killed when barriers collapsed during an FA Cup tie?

21 What feat did Chuck Yeager achieve in a Bell X-1 rocket plane in October 1947?

22 What phrase did Winston Churchill coin to describe the division between east and west In postwar Europe?

23 Which tough-minded anti-Nazi became chancellor of the new German Federal Republic in 1949?

24 Which famous Jewish refugee ship was prevented by the British from docking at Haifa in 1947?

25 Name the newspaper threatened with suppression in 1942 for publishing a cartoon interpreted as critical.

26 Which Polish prime minister was killed in an air crash at Gibraltar in 1943?

27 What name was given to Germany's last great counter-attack of World War 2, through the Ardennes forest?

28 Who joined the Labour cabinet as its youngest member in September 1947?

29 What major new alliance was formed between eight western countries in 1949?

30 In 1948, who was out for a duck in his last Test when four runs would have given him a batting average of 100?

HE WON'T SECURE VICTORY THAT WAY.

Answers on page 205

Knowall's question:

Which new ensemble was described as "The nation's Rockingest Rhythm Group" in 1954?

BUDDY HOLLY AND THE CRICKETS !!!

1 Who was elected President of the Fifth French Republic in 1958?

2 Which two famous British car companies agreed to merge in November 1951?

3 What team won the sensational 1953 "Stanley Matthews" FA Cup final 4-3?

4 In 1955, the man called "the most famous scientist of all time" died in New Jersey. Who was he?

5 What was stolen by Scottish Nationalists from Westminster Abbey in 1950?

6 In 1952, which notorious but popular "First Lady" died of cancer in Argentina aged 33?

7 What agreement forged Europe's Eastern Bloc nations into a new alliance in 1955?

8 Which star was effectively banned from returning to the USA after leaving to promote his film *Limelight*?

9 What Kenyan terrorist group challenged British rule in the early 1950s?

10 When did postwar rationing finally end in Britain: 1951, 1952, 1953, 1954, 1955?

11 Which US senator and vice-presidential candidate was accused of misusing campaign funds in 1952?

12 Name the Queen Mother's horse which fell on the run-in with the 1956 Grand National all but won.

13 Who remarked "I think it will be a great experience for me" when he joined the US Army in 1958?

14 Which driver became the first Briton to win Italy's prestigious Mille Miglia motor race?

15 What disease introduced from Australia devastated Britain's wild rabbit population in the 1950s?

16 Where was Princess Elizabeth when she learned of her father's death in 1952?

17 In 1955, where exactly did Walt Disney open his Disneyland theme park?

18 What caused Eniwetok atoll in the Pacific to vanish completely in 1952?

19 In which year did ITV begin broadcasting in Britain: 1954, 1955, 1956, 1957, 1958?

20 Which prominent general was dismissed by President Truman in 1951 for making political statements?

21 Who died on Loch Ness attempting a new water speed record when his jet-powered boat *Crusader* crashed?

22 Name America's then highest paid singer, who made his British debut at the London Palladium in 1950.

23 In 1955, a horrific crash at which French motor race killed 80 people?

24 The first Olympic Games to be held in the southern hemisphere took place in what city?

25 Which cleric became the first president of the new republic of Cyprus in 1959?

26 Name three of the four "Goons" whose radio show built up a huge following in the 1950s.

27 Which feared dictator died of a cerebral haemorrhage on 5 March 1953?

28 To which Berkshire destination did CND march from London each Easter, starting in 1958?

29 In 1957, the so-called "high priest of haute couture" died in Italy. Who was he?

30 Which country rose in popular revolt against Soviet domination in 1956?

THINK ASTRONOMY RATHER THAN ENTOMOLOGY.

Answers on page 206

Knowall's question:

What great Yorkshire and England fast bowler announced his retirement from cricket in November 1968?

BRIAN STATHAM !!!

1 Which 23-year-old leading dancer with the Kirov Ballet Company defected to the West in 1961?

2 What Sunday newspaper did Rupert Murdoch buy in 1969 after a bitter takeover battle with Robert Maxwell?

3 Into which country did President Johnson "send the Marines" in 1965?

4 Who said of his family's cash worries in 1969: "We sold off a small yacht and I may have to give up polo."?

5 Which famous Italian movie couple faced bigamy charges in 1962?

6 What draconian event did Chairman Mao Tse-tung officially proclaim in August 1966?

7 In 1960, who detected "a wind of change" blowing through the continent of Africa?

8 How did Czech student Jan Palach protest against Russian occupation in Prague's Wenceslas Square?

9 Name the Texas governor in President Kennedy's car when they were both shot in November 1963.

10 In 1966, who met in Rome's Sistine Chapel to heal a 400-year-old rift?

11 What country considered part of France for 132 years was granted independence in 1962?

12 Major Edward White became the first American astronaut to do what in June 1965?

13 Which D. H. Lawrence novel banned for over 30 years was declared legal in a celebrated case in 1960?

14 In what Los Angeles district did serious race riots break out in August 1965?

15 What memorable slogan accompanied an attempt to improve British productivity in 1968?

16 Which former fighter-pilot became prime minister of Southern Rhodesia in 1964?

17 What did the House of Commons abolish in Britain by 355 votes to 170 in 1964?

18 Name the breakaway province of Nigeria occupied by Government troops amid great suffering in 1968.

19 The mighty Zambesi River was tamed by which dam and hydro-electric project, completed in 1960?

20 Which two rival gangs of young people regularly fought running battles at seaside resorts in the mid-1960s?

21 In 1966, which Briton became the first driver to win motor racing's Indianapolis 500 at his first attempt?

22 What major country left the British Commonwealth in May 1961 after becoming a republic?

23 Which satirical magazine backed by comedian Peter Cook began publishing In 1962?

24 In 1967, what 100-1 outsider won the Grand National after a serious pile-up at the 23rd fence?

25 What European capital city experienced its "worst street fighting since 1944" in May 1968?

26 In 1965, what did fashion shops start selling to adults free of tax as children's garments?

27 Who was arrested and convicted of murdering Senator Robert Kennedy in 1968?

28 The engagement of which commoner to Princess Margaret was announced in February 1960?

29 When was the ban on professional tennis players at Wimbledon lifted: 1960, 1962, 1964, 1966, 1968?

30 In 1967, which 65-year-old completed a solo world circumnavigation in his yacht *Gypsy Moth IV*?

Answers on page 206

Knowall's question:

The American space shuttle first took off in 1977 with a little help from what?

ITS ENGINES !!!

1 In December 1979, what country was invaded by Soviet troops?

2 Who succeeded Gamal Abdel Nasser as president of Egypt in 1970?

3 The face of the English countryside was ravaged by what tree disease in the 1970s?

4 Who blundered onto TV screens in 1975 as the manic owner-manager of a Torquay hotel?

5 What Central American capital city was devastated by an earthquake that killed over 10,000 in 1972?

6 Which South African black consciousness leader died in 1977 after being severely beaten in a police cell?

7 Presenter Bill Grundy was suspended after a punk group ran amok on ITV's *Today* show. Which group?

8 In what year did Britain join the European Economic Community: 1970, 1971, 1972, 1973, 1974, 1975?

9 Who was the wife of President Juan Perón of Argentina, herself deposed as president in 1976?

10 Dustbins overflowing, patients turned away, corpses unburied. What was this period in 1978-79 called?

11 Which equestrienne was named Sportswoman of the Year in 1971 by the British Sportswriters Association?

12 What new cut-price transatlantic air service was launched by Freddie Laker in 1977?

13 By what names were Haitian father-and-son dictators François and Jean-Claude Duvalier known?

14 In what bizarre manner did Bulgarian defector Georgi Markov die in 1978?

15 What significant treaty did presidents Leonid Brezhnev and Jimmy Carter sign in June 1979?

16 Who had President Nixon bugged on the celebrated "Watergate Tapes" that emerged in 1973?

17 In 1970, who became the first Briton to win the US Open golf championship in 50 years?

18 Who was killed when his boat was blown up by the IRA off Mullaghmore in 1979?

19 In 1972, thousands of Asians fled Idi Amin's terror in which African country?

20 Name the temperamental player who became America's first world chess champion in 1972.

21 Which dictator who had ruled Portugal since the 1920s died aged 81 in 1970?

22 Who was elected as Rhodesia's first-ever black prime minister in 1979?

23 What Humberside chemical plant was destroyed by a massive blast in June 1974?

24 In what year did bicentennial fever grip the United States of America, coming to a climax on 4 July?

25 Which expatriate tramp achieved ultimate respectability when knighted by the Queen in 1975?

26 In the 1970s, which brutal leader was responsible for Cambodia's "killing fields"?

27 At which American university were four students protesting against the Vietnam war shot dead in 1970?

28 Name the young British athlete who captured world 800m, mile and 1,500m records in 1975.

29 Which legendary FBI chief died in 1972 after serving eight presidents in nearly 50 years?

30 In 1977, which horse became the first ever to win the Grand National three times?

HE NEEDS A MEMORY LIKE AN ELEPHANT'S.

Answers on page 206

Knowall's question:

Which "unknown senator from Indiana" became George Bush's running mate in the 1988 presidential election?

SPIRO AGNEW !!!

1 Who did Mark David Chapman shoot dead in New York on 8 December 1980?

2 In 1985, international media mogul Rupert Murdoch purchased a half share in what Hollywood film studio?

3 Where did the Chinese army savagely crush a freedom demonstration in June 1989?

4 Who said "if this is justice I'm a banana" after massive libel damages were awarded against *Private Eye*?

5 Tennis returned to the Olympics in 1988 after a long break. Who won the women's singles gold medal?

6 Who was sacked as Moscow's Communist Party boss in 1987 for criticising Mikhail Gorbachev?

7 Which country's London embassy was stormed by the SAS in 1980 to end a terrorist occupation?

8 What significant "first" was achieved by physicist Sally Ride in 1983?

9 The BMX bicycle craze arrived in Britain in 1984. What does BMX stand for?

10 American aircraft attacked which country in April 1986 as a retaliation for "terrorist activities"?

11 The Clapham train crash and Lockerbie bombing took place in: Jan 1987, Dec 1988, Mar 1989, Feb 1990?

12 Name the separatist group who rebelled against the Sri Lankan government throughout the 1980s?

13 The "King of the Redcoats" opened his first holiday camp in 1932 and died in 1980. Who was he?

14 Which Cornish lifeboat sank with the loss of its crew when attempting an impossible rescue in 1981?

15 What political party surprisingly won 15% of votes cast in Britain's 1989 European parliamentary elections?

16 What expensive-to-win sporting trophy finally left the USA in 1983 after 132 years?

17 What name was given to two rock concerts in Britain and America that raised £40 million for famine relief?

18 In 1988, a massive earthquake near the Turkish border killed over 100,000 people in which country?

19 Who led striking shipyard workers to victory over the Polish government at Gdansk in 1980?

20 What group was driven from its Beirut bases in 1981 by Israeli forces?

21 Which Philippines opposition leader was shot dead on a plane when he returned from exile in 1983?

22 Where were 94 soccer fans tragically killed during an FA Cup semi-final in April 1989?

23 In 1982, who was awakened in the middle of the night by a request for a cigarette from Michael Fagan?

24 Name the Thames pleasureboat sunk by the dredger *Bowbelle* in 1989 with the loss of over 60 lives.

25 After what natural disaster did the Meteorological Office admit "we could have got it better"?

26 Despite pleas from government, the British Olympic Association decided NOT to do what in March 1980?

27 Which jockey won the Grand National on Aldaniti in 1981 after winning his battle against cancer?

28 Name the woman PC killed by shooting from the Libyan Embassy in April 1984.

29 In 1986, which prominent Soviet dissident returned to Moscow after internal exile at Gorky?

30 Where was the Berlin Wall finally breached officially on 22 December 1989?

HE MAKES YOU QUAKE.

Answers on page 206

Knowall's question:

The Rev. Canaan Banana was the first president of which country that became independent in 1980?

THE DOMINICAN REPUBLIC !!!

1 Who became mayor of Carmel, California in 1986 at a salary of $200 per month?

2 Which ice-cool tennis ace won the Wimbledon's men's singles title for the fifth successive year in 1980?

3 In 1983, a massive car bomb destroyed the United States Embassy in which city?

4 What so-called "crack American force" failed miserably to release hostages held by Iran in 1980?

5 In 1989, a state of emergency was declared after what disaster that claimed nearly 300 lives in America?

6 Who became leader of the Labour Party after James Callaghan's resignation in 1980?

7 Where in Northern Ireland did an IRA bomb kill 11 people on Remembrance Day in 1987?

8 Which comic's performance in the film *Being There* was hailed as his finest, just before he died in 1980?

9 In 1989, which became the first Soviet Bloc country to appoint a non-communist prime minister?

10 Who succeeded in becoming president of France at the third attempt in 1981?

11 Outside what Yorkshire coking plant did police and striking miners fight a pitched battle in 1984?

12 What terrible error did Captain Will Rogers of the USS *Vincennes* make in 1988?

13 Collectively, who were Patrick Armstrong, Gerard Conlon, Paul Hill and Carole Richardson?

14 Who was the "stalking horse" knight who challenged Margaret Thatcher for the Tory leadership?

15 Indian troops stormed which Sikh holy shrine in June 1984, with the loss of over 800 lives?

16 What was significant about Oxford's win in the 1981 University Boat Race?

17 In what Irish city did 49 people die in a discotheque fire on St Valentine's Day in 1980?

18 Name the master-batsman sacked by cricket county Yorkshire at the age of 45 in 1986.

19 Troops provided what after 2,500 public service workers were suspended for taking industrial acton in 1989?

20 What name was given to SDP founders Roy Jenkins, David Owen, Bill Rodgers and Shirley Williams in 1981?

21 In 1980, who thwarted a right-wing coup in Spain by ordering in the army and addressing the nation on TV?

22 A Luton Town fan and half of one of TV's best-loved comedy duos died in May 1983. Who was he?

23 Name the Archbishop of Canterbury criticised in 1989 for taking vespers with the Pope in Rome.

24 Which great radio cricket commentator retired after the Centenary Test Match at Lord's in 1980?

25 Who was Chiang Ching, dragged screaming from court convicted of "counter-revolutionary crime" in 1980?

26 What did Europe retain at Muirfield Village, Ohio in September 1987?

27 On what island did scrap dealers land in March 1982 and precipitate a crisis by raising the Argentinian flag?

28 Who resigned as leader of the Liberal Party in 1988 after 12 years in the job?

29 What company owned the *Herald of Free Enterprise* that sank in 1987 with massive loss of life?

30 Which 60-year-old "fashion empress" and store boss died after a fall at her home in 1985?

IT'S TIME HE LEARNED HIS R TO Z.

Answers on page 207

QUIZ NUMBER 14

Knowall's question:

Californian researchers have claimed that listening to Mozart sonatas could improve what human faculty?

HEARING !!!

1 Who firmly stated in January 1991 that the hated poll tax would not be abolished?

2 Which major Japanese town was devastated by an earthquake in January 1995?

3 In 1993 the Native Title Act restored land rights to which group of native people?

4 Who was arrested following an incident during Michael Jackson's performance at the 1996 Brit Awards?

5 Brightlingsea drew attention in 1995 when it was the scene of long-running demonstrations. Against what?

6 What spectacular exhibition was staged in the Spanish city of Seville in 1992?

7 The people of which country decided to reject the idea of membership of the European Community in 1994?

8 Who captained the rebel cricket tour of South Africa which was eventually cancelled in the spring of 1990?

9 When was Boris Yeltsin first elected president of the Russian Federation: 1990, 1991, 1992, 1993, 1994?

10 Which threatened author made a surprise appearance at a U2 concert in 1993?

11 In 1996, which three international cricketers were locked into a court battle over allegations of cheating?

12 In 1993, which "madam to the stars" sensationally went on trial in Los Angeles?

13 Why did John White suffer the disappointment of his professional life in April 1993?

14 What was the name of Coca-Cola's new soft drink, launched in 1994 amid a blaze of publicity?

15 Whose expensive $200 haircut on an aircraft caused a serious political rumpus?

16 Jurist Thurgood Marshall died in the USA in 1993, aged 85. What was his claim to fame?

17 Who became the first female Speaker of the House of Commons in 1992?

18 In 1996, which familiar British figure reappeared in the advertising guise of a "devil with red eyes"?

19 Who was the only survivor of a New York discotheque fire in 1990 which claimed 87 lives?

20 Name the political party mounting an increasingly vociferous campaign for an independent Wales.

21 A 1996 feasibility study examined what major new link between Carlisle and Newcastle?

22 The French government disbanded a long-established specialist military unit in 1993. Which one?

23 In which northern British prison did a major riot erupt in April 1990, followed by an orgy of damage?

24 In March 1993 the International Chess Federation disqualified which two grand masters?

25 What was the noteworthy supersonic aviation "first" achieved by airline pilot Barbara Harmer?

26 Which royal residence was severely damaged by fire in November 1992?

27 In March 1996, many eyes turned towards Hyakutake, but what is it?

28 Alexander Lebed brokered a 1996 ceasefire in an internal war in which Russian republic?

29 What was it that O. J. Simpson couldn't get on that helped get O. J. Simpson off?

30 In 1995, where did Berkshire protestors have to come down from the trees and make way for the diggers?

HE'S NOT VERY BRIGHT.

Answers on page 207

Knowall's question:

Which piece of 19th-century technology was sold for £7.7 million at Christie's in 1993?

STEPHENSON'S ROCKET !!!

TRIVIA KING

1 The long-established presenter of BBC Radio 4's *News Quiz* bowed out in 1996. Who is he?

2 3 August 1990 was the hottest day recorded in Britain with a temperature of: 35.3°C, 36.7°C, 37.1°C, 38.4°C?

3 Of what atrocity was blind Sheikh Abdul Rahman convicted in 1996?

4 The European president of which company was fired for a "free flights" promotion that misfired badly?

5 Name two of the three countries that joined the European Union in 1995.

6 Which European capital hosted the historic Middle East summit which took place in November 1991?

7 After a long career without an Oscar, who won two as director and actor in *Unforgiven*?

8 Who was the president of South Africa when Nelson Mandela was released?

9 What did the voyeuristic video banned by the British High Court in September 1996 depict?

10 Which "evil empire" officially ceased to exist in December 1991?

11 American scientists claimed to have discovered fossil evidence of life on which planet in August 1996?

12 Which international statesman received the Nobel Peace Prize in October 1990?

13 In which country did urban terrorists release deadly nerve gas on trains in 1995?

14 Which female climber managed to conquer Everest only to die on K2 shortly afterwards?

15 Why did John Major decide to sue the *New Statesman* for libel in January 1993?

16 For what thoroughly modern activity was a new Scout badge introduced in 1996?

17 What did France persist in conducting in 1995, despite vociferous international opposition?

18 Alleged sibling rivalry led to the abandonment of which mega-group's American tour in September 1996?

19 Which well-known publishing "bird" reached the age of 60 in 1995?

20 In 1993, which building became the focal point of an attempted anti-government coup in Russia?

21 In 1996, Roderick Wright resigned from what post over allegations of affairs with women?

22 Which exclusive London store is owned by the new proprietor of *Punch* magazine, revived in 1996?

23 What new skill did Norma Major acquire as a result of her many visits to Chequers?

24 Where in the American south-west did hard-line sheriff Joe Arpaio establish female chain gangs in 1996?

25 After losing millions, what did EuroDisney become in an attempt to revive its flagging fortunes?

26 In which Cheshire town did IRA bombs mow down children and Mother's Day shoppers?

27 Where did the historic handshake between Yasser Arafat and Yitzhak Rabin take place in 1993?

28 Who participated in the three-way battle to become Conservative leader and prime minister in 1990?

29 Who was waiting to greet embarrassed US Marines when they stormed ashore in Somalia in 1992?

30 Which "everyday story of country folk" celebrated 40 years on the air in 1990?

DON'T COUNT ON IT.

Answers on page 207

Knowall's question:

Which unfortunate American was relieved of his most private part by an irate wife?

TRICKY DICKY !!!

1 What do the letters UHT stand for?

2 In 1985, what was Shakin' Stevens' seasonal No. 1?

3 Which gangster movie only featured kids?

4 Nijinsky – a famous dancer and what else?

5 Who was Annie Lennox's partner in the Eurythmics?

6 What did Arthur Scargill call his new party in 1995?

7 Earth adapts in order to survive. What theory?

8 What is nitro-cellulose (gun cotton)?

9 Which actor played the butler in *Upstairs, Downstairs*?

10 The lev is the currency of which European country?

11 What kind of weapon is a modern Tomahawk?

12 Which divorcee did Tim Laurence marry in 1992?

13 L. Frank Baum wrote which children's classic in 1903?

14 Which writer boasts the longest entry in *Who's Who*?

15 What is the EEC's most densely populated country?

16 Where is the Sea of Tranquility?

17 Name the Old English sheepdog in The Perishers.

18 In which county is Cannock Chase?

19 Nathuram Godse became infamous in 1948 for what?

20 Which Irish singer tore up a picture of the Pope on TV?

21 What was Soviet President Khrushchev's first name?

22 ASA or ISO numbers measure what?

23 What is the official language of Andorra?

24 In which country was the 1900 Boxer Rising?

25 Who was born Agnes Bojaxhiu in Yugoslavia in 1910?

26 *Message in a Bottle* was a 1979 hit for which group?

27 Which city ceased to be the capital of Brazil in 1960?

28 Which Japanese car firm was first to invest in the UK?

29 In trades union parlance, what did OMOV mean?

30 What sporting device has a lift end, dingle and elbow?

WAS SHE A HAIRDRESSER?

Answers on page 207

Knowall's question:

Which two pioneers of sex research were divorced in 1993?

MR & MRS KINSEY !!!

1 Which famous sportsman did Jemima Goldsmith, daughter of Sir James, marry in 1995?

2 Martha Reeves and the Vandellas twice made the charts in the 1960s with which classic pop song?

3 What was the name originally given by Sue Townsend to her teenage diarist Adrian Mole?

4 In 1996 the world's longest ship, SS *Norway*, had a refit in Southampton. What was her name until 1992?

5 How many trips does the average British milk bottle make: 12, 22, 32, 42 or 52?

6 What industrial "umpiring" organisation was set up by the Labour government in 1975?

7 Which country produces roughly three-quarters of the world's mined gold?

8 What links the Dolomite, Herald, Spitfire, Stag, Toledo and Vitesse?

9 By what title is the Crown's chief law officer in England and Wales known?

10 What has been the world's best-selling toy in the 1990s: Action Man, Barbie, Lego or Play-Doh?

11 Which leading actor, born Michael Shalhouz, later became a bridge correspondent for *The Observer*?

12 Which nation drinks the most coffee: the Americans, Brazilians, Finns, French, Greeks, Italians or Turks?

13 Who succeeded Cardinal Heenan as Catholic Archbishop of Westminster in 1976?

14 What's the link: Leonard Cohen, Joni Mitchell, Neil Young, Bryan Adams, Celine Dion, Alanou Morrisette?

15 What were the lone three fighter-planes that defended Malta in World War 2 nicknamed?

16 Who moved from the anchor role on Radio 2's *Sports Report* to host the 4pm-7pm slot on Radio 5 Live?

17 Name the British politician who made the controversial "rivers of blood" speech in 1968.

18 With which novel did Kazuo Ishiguro win the Whitbread Literary Award for fiction in 1986?

19 At the United Nations, how many countries are permanent members of the Security Council?

20 In which 1932 film did Greta Garbo actually speak the oft-quoted words "I want to be alone."?

21 Which is the largest of the four provinces in the Republic of Ireland?

22 Which "first lady" worked as an editor for the American publishing houses of Viking and Doubleday?

23 Name the children's TV programme that featured Bungle, George and Zippi.

24 Which East African leader gave himself the title "Conqueror of the British Empire"?

25 Name the prolific Detroit-based record label founded by Gordon Berry Jnr.

26 For what principal purpose are UHF (ultra-high frequency) radio waves used?

27 With which of the performing arts would you associate the Russian Sergei Diaghilev?

28 Which country was called the Dutch East Indies until it gained independence in 1949?

29 What was the yacht, skippered by Dennis Conner, that took the America's Cup back to the USA in 1987?

30 Name the Dutchman whose company built military aircraft for the Germans during World War 1.

WHAT KIND OF RESPONSE IS THAT?

Answers on page 208

Knowall's question:

In 1996, which US state became the first to sanction "chemical castration" for persistent child sex offenders?

VIRGINIA !!!

ASK ME ANOTHER

1 Norma Desmond is the name of the lead character in which successful film and stage musical?

2 What name did Stalingrad, scene of appalling loss of life during the winter of 1942-43, adopt in 1961?

3 Pablo Casals was considered to be one of the century's greatest virtuosos. On what instrument?

4 What is special about the two words "abstemious" and "facetious"?

5 Which hugely profitable British company announced in September 1996 it was to shed 5,000 jobs?

6 Who won the Eurovision Song Contest in 1993 for Ireland with *In Your Eyes*?

7 Suez is at the southern end of the Suez Canal. Which city is situated at the northern end of the waterway?

8 What famous venue hosted its last event in 1996 – the Davis Cup match between Britain and Egypt?

9 Which EC country has the highest percentage of working women: Austria, Denmark, Italy, Spain, UK?

10 Name one of Kylie Minogue's three No. 1 singles in Britain after *I Should Be So Lucky* in 1988.

11 What is the profession of Cherie Blair, wife of the Labour Party leader?

12 Which Asian country won Miss World in 1985 and 1994 – and hosted the contest in 1996?

13 In *Coronation Street*, who was played by Lynne Carol: Minnie Caldwell, Martha Longhurst or Ena Sharples?

14 Peach melba derives its name from Australian soprano Helen Porter Mitchell. What was her "stage" name?

15 What do members of the House of Commons refer to as "another place"?

16 What is the odd one out: electron, micron, neutron or proton?

17 Which bearded German "orchestra" leader had 60 chart albums between 1967 and 1995?

18 What was the title of Arthur Ransome's most famous children's book, published in 1937?

19 In August 1996, which firm proposed a takeover of Carlsberg-Tetley to make it Britain's biggest brewer?

20 In what 1970s TV series did Michael Douglas (as cop Karl Malden's sidekick) first make his mark?

21 Who was the minister for education and science in the Thatcher government from 1981 to 1986?

22 When did the National Lottery start: Sept. 1994, Nov. 1994, Feb. 1995, May 1995 or Sept. 1995?

23 Which country in Europe consistently records the worst figures for road accidents?

24 What E. M. Forster novel, filmed in 1984, centres on the friendship of a teacher and a doctor?

25 What royal event did the people of Britain celebrate on 6 May 1935?

26 On a clothing label, what symbol indicates that a garment should be dry-cleaned?

27 Which London-born actress was played by Julie Andrews in the 1968 musical film *Star!*?

28 A famous Native American princess is buried at Gravesend, in Kent. Who is she?

29 In what year was the Greater London Council abolished: 1980, 1982, 1884, 1986 or 1988?

30 Which British foreign secretary resigned after Argentina invaded the Falklands in 1982?

HE'S JUST DREAMING.

Answers on page 208

Knowall's question:

What colour is produced by dyeing wool with dandelion: brown, magenta, purple, orange or yellow?

YELLOW !!!

1 What was the top film of the 1970s: *Grease, Jaws, Star Wars, Superman*?

2 Is the District Line on a London Underground map: brown, green, red, yellow?

3 Which one of these birds is protected in Britain: cormorant, rook, starling, wood pigeon?

4 Which of the following titles is the highest ranking: baron, duke, earl, marquess?

5 What is 70°F on the Centigrade scale: 18.4°, 19.6°, 20.2°, 21.8°?

6 What is the international car index mark for India: I, IA, IDA, IND?

7 Which gemstone is associated with the month of July: diamond, emerald, ruby, sapphire?

8 What is the most frequent word in written English: and, in, of, the?

9 Which of the following nuts has the most calories: almond, brazil, peanut, walnut?

10 Which continental shoe size is equivalent to a UK size 9: 41, 42, 43, 44?

11 On what date does All Souls day fall: 25 January, 24 June, 8 September, 2 November?

12 What gift is associated with a 13th wedding anniversary: crystal, ivory, lace, silk?

13 On 1 March when is sunrise in London: 6.15am, 6.30am, 6.45am, 7am?

14 Which spice is derived from the crocus: cinnamon, cloves, nutmeg, saffron?

15 Dry air at sea level contains mostly which gas: argon, carbon dioxide, nitrogen, oxygen?

16 Which one of the following publications is weekly: *Car, Country Life, Private Eye, Reader's Digest*?

17 How many countries are headed by a sovereign: 15, 27, 46, 62?

18 In which university is the Bodleian Library: Cambridge, Edinburgh, London, Oxford?

19 Which shotgun has the smallest bore size: 4 bore, 12 bore, 16 bore, 28 bore?

20 Which is the largest youth organisation in the UK: Boy Scouts, Brownies, Cubs, Girl Guides?

21 How many acres are there in a square mile: 560, 600, 640, 680?

22 Which planet is fourth from the Sun: Earth, Jupiter, Mars, Venus?

23 What colour is the wax covering Edam cheese: cream, red, white, yellow?

24 Which country has the most universities: France, India, UK, USA?

25 Which country had the first woman prime minister: Argentina, Ceylon (Sri Lanka), India, Israel?

26 How many quires make a ream: 10, 20, 30, 40?

27 Which of these London galleries is south of the Thames: Hayward, Royal Academy, Serpentine, Tate?

28 In which year did Radio 1 start broadcasting: 1961, 1963, 1965, 1967?

29 Which one of these writers is English: Ian McEwan, Norman Mailer, Henry Miller, Alice Munro?

30 How many strings does a harp have: 11, 24, 35, 47?

ANOTHER MAGNIFICENT FAILURE.

Answers on page 208

Knowall's question:

What sensational fate befell
Metropolitan Police Commissioner
Sir William Horwood in 1922?

HE WAS
ARRESTED !!!

1 Whose Far Eastern trading activities led to the downfall of Barings Bank?

2 Which two prominent American politicians had affairs with Marilyn Monroe while holding office?

3 What headline-making divorce became absolute on 28 August 1996?

4 Which famous French actress had her right leg amputated in 1915?

5 Name the minister who resigned in 1988 after boldly claiming that most eggs contained salmonella?

6 New Zealand horsewoman Heather Tonkin made a paternity claim against whom in 1991?

7 On which top-rated show did the Beatles make their American television debut in 1964?

8 Whose "first freely elected Marxist government in the West" was overthrown with the CIA's help in 1973?

9 Which American president was ultimately brought down by the Watergate Affair?

10 Who made world headlines by completing the world's first human heart transplant operation in 1967?

11 Who received £2 in damages when a medical firm used part of his poem *If* without permission in an ad?

12 Which singer became an enduringly popular figure after his violent death in Iowa on 3 February 1959?

13 Born in Jersey; the Prince of Wales' mistress; naturalised American; died in 1929. Who was she?

14 Which former KGB chief became president of the USSR in 1983?

15 Of what country was Paul Doumer, assassinated at a literary function in 1932, the president?

16 Who was stripped of his Olympic 100 metres crown in 1988 after testing positive for a banned drug?

17 Which much-loved but troubled British comedian committed suicide in 1968 at the age of 44?

18 In the 1970s, Holland's Prince Bernhard suffered a bribery scandal involving what US defence contractor?

19 In 1980 which Austrian-born conservationist, who told the story of lioness Elsa, was murdered in Africa?

20 Whose novel published in 1921 caused a storm of controversy for featuring two nude men wrestling?

21 Name the leader of France's wartime Vichy regime who was executed for treason in 1945.

22 In 1979, which Hollywood actor was sued by girlfriend Michelle Trioloa in the first great "palimony" case?

23 In 1953, what humanoid fossil "found" in a Sussex gravel pit in 1912 was exposed as a clever hoax?

24 Which Nazi war criminal was kidnapped by Israelis from Argentina and hanged after a trial in 1962?

25 It eventually became public that a US wartime general had an affair with his British driver. Which general?

26 Name the Oscar-winning actress who made headlines for her passionate anti-Vietnam War activities.

27 Which Palestinian-born engineer became chairman of the PLO but renounced violence in 1988?

28 Lieutenant William Calley was accused of overseeing the massacre of 500 South Vietnamese civilians. Where?

29 Name the dignified black American tennis player who died in 1993 after contracting Aids from a transfusion.

30 Spy Anthony Blunt was disgraced when exposed as the "Fourth Man". Name two of the other three spies.

THAT'S A POISONOUS THOUGHT.

Answers on page 208

Knowall's question:

Which ex-minister stood against Margaret Thatcher in the first ballot which led to her resignation as PM?

JOHN MAJOR !!!

1 In 1929, who ordered the infamous "St Valentine's Day Massacre" in Chicago?

2 Who opened London's first birth control clinic in 1921 amid a storm of controversy and bitter opposition?

3 The San Francisco publisher of which American beat poet was sensationally tried for issuing his works?

4 Which Ohio-born American president's administration was tainted by serious corruption in his Cabinet?

5 In 1990, which famous actor's son was arrested for shooting dead his half-sister's lover Dag Drollet?

6 In a recorded conversation between James Gilbey and Princess Diana, by what pet name did he address her?

7 Which roisterous Irish dramatist who wrote the play *Borstal Boy* was arrested in 1939 for IRA involvement?

8 The rectitude of which RAF chief who organised the bombing of Germany has been repeatedly questioned?

9 Which actress who died in 1990 was described as "the world's most famous star" 40 years after she retired?

10 Where did Mary Jo Kopechne's death by drowning end Edward Kennedy's presidential ambitions in 1969?

11 In October 1920, whose Armistice Day burial in Westminster Abbey was approved by George V?

12 In 1978, which former Italian prime minister was kidnapped and murdered by Red Brigade terrorists?

13 Which controversial Australian feminist wrote *The Female Eunuch* in 1970?

14 Who died shortly after excavating Tutankhamun's tomb in 1922, fuelling the myth of the "Pharoah's Curse"?

15 "The world's largest bank fraud" was unmasked in 1991 when what bank collapsed?

16   In 1982, which Israeli leader's invasion of Lebanon was meant to last 72 hours rather than three years?

17   Which cabinet minister resigned in the early 1960s after his affair with Christine Keeler was revealed?

18   Which famous Hollywood personality's body was stolen from its Swiss grave in March 1978?

19   Name the famous Argentinian medical student who fought alongside Castro in Cuba and died in Bolivia.

20   Which 1920s star was jailed for 10 days and fined $500 for indecency for her role in the Broadway show *Sex*?

21   Name the former fighter-pilot and leading Nazi who cheated the gallows by swallowing cyanide in 1946.

22   America's top World War 2 fighter ace was killed in 1945 when his Lockheed P-80 crashed. Name him.

23   Which dubious 1978 land deal in the Ozarks cast a shadow over Bill Clinton's presidency?

24   Who, with the Prince of Wales as best man, married heiress Edwina Ashley in 1922's "Wedding of the Year"?

25   Which scandal-ridden Hollywood star who made her name in *The Wizard of Oz* died of a drug overdose?

26   Name the Colombian drug baron shot to death in 1993 after strolling out of prison two years earlier.

27   The 1966 best-selling "non-fiction novel" *In Cold Blood* about a Kansas murder case was by which writer?

28   In 1996, whose father was arraigned on massive tax evasion charges in Germany?

29   Who was Stalin's deputy and feared secret police chief, summarily charged with espionage and shot in 1953?

30   Which scandal-ridden British peer died in Manila in 1991, leaving two rival sons and heirs?

NICE ONE, TARZAN.

Answers on page 209

Knowall's question:

Which American diplomat was jailed in 1950 after microfilms of secret documents were found in a pumpkin?

HENRY KISSINGER ???

1 How did the unfortunate John Welby make judicial history at Strangeways prison in 1964?

2 Which Russian foreign minister sensationally resigned in 1990 and later became president of Georgia?

3 Shares buying in which company resulted in false claims of insider dealing against writer Jeffrey Archer?

4 Whose daughter is Alina Fernandez Revuelta, granted political asylum in the USA in 1993?

5 Which famous American newspaper published the hoax story about eight-year-old heroin addict "Jimmy"?

6 Name the dictator ousted by American troops and later put on trial in Florida for drug-trafficking.

7 Who mounted a public attack on *EastEnders* in 1987, claiming the soap opera put the nation at moral risk?

8 In 1970, what uninhibited London sex revue devised by Kenneth Tynan failed to generate the anticipated fury?

9 Which female blues singer died in 1959 after a life ruined by professional frustration and heroin addiction?

10 Which US vice-president resigned in 1973 after tax evasion charges were levelled against him?

11 Which playboy king of Egypt was forced to abdicate in 1952 after a series of arms scandals?

12 Name one of the two British comedians who made news by dying within a day of each other in 1992.

13 Which 88-year-old American newspaper tycoon whose lurid private life often made the news died in 1951?

14 In 1973, which peer and minister resigned after being caught in bed with two women, smoking marijuana?

15 Who pretended to be a peer's daughter and stole £3 million from a medical charity in the early 1990s?

16 In 1989, newspaper editors Andrew Neil and Donald Trelford dated which former Miss India?

17 In 1912, what was Captain Smith's decidedly unfortunate claim to fame?

18 Which high-profile entertainer died when the plane carrying him to France in 1944 crashed in fog?

19 Name the Pakistani prime minister sacked in 1990 amid accusations of constitutional manipulation?

20 Irish nationalist Tomas MacSwiney died after a hunger strike in 1920. Of which town was he the lord mayor?

21 Who went missing, presumed drowned, on a Miami beach in 1974, only to be arrested later in Australia?

22 Which Russian writer was expelled as a "traitor" from the Soviet Writers' Union for his book *Dr Zhivago*?

23 Who was the controversial founder of *John Bull* weekly and MP jailed for a victory bond fraud in 1922?

24 In 1987, former SS officer Klaus Barbie was jailed for wartime crimes in France. What was his nickname?

25 Which TV evangelist was jailed for 45 years in 1989 after admitting "I have sinned. I have made mistakes."?

26 Which Enid Blyton character lost his "golliwog" friends in 1987 as political correctness invaded publishing?

27 Who was the British nuclear scientist sensationally convicted as a Russian spy in 1950 after an FBI tip?

28 Name the notoriously corrupt governor of Louisiana who was murdered by a political opponent in 1935.

29 Whose moving diary of her time spent hiding from the Germans was posthumously published after the war?

30 Which mayor of Washington D.C. did the FBI secretly photograph smoking "crack" cocaine in 1990?

YOU SOUND LIKE A REAL SNAKE.

Answers on page 209

Knowall's question:

Who did Beatle Paul
McCartney marry?

JANE ASHER !!!

1 Which French actress and animal lover married film director Roger Vadim?

2 Which Chelsea-supporting Minister for the Arts and Sport had an affair with Antonia de Sancha?

3 For which twice-divorced American woman did Edward VIII give up his crown?

4 Which famously well-preserved English actress was first married to Anthony Newley?

5 Liza Minnelli is the child of director Vincente Minnelli and which Hollywood star?

6 Supermodel Cindy Crawford married which handsome American actor?

7 Who was photographed in the South of France having her royal toes kissed by lover John Bryan?

8 Which Hollywood ladies' man had a celebrated affair with Madonna before marrying Annette Bening?

9 Which English actor and director was married to Oscar-winning actress Emma Thompson?

10 Which tennis player has had love affairs with Barbra Streisand and Brooke Shields?

11 Which actress was the long-standing love of American film star Spencer Tracy?

12 Which English novelist and poet eloped with and married Frieda von Richthofen?

13 Actress and director's daughter Anjelica Huston had a 17-year affair with which Hollywood hell-raiser?

14 Which American singer and actress was married to and sang in partnership with Sonny Bono?

15 With which famous American politician did Gennifer Flowers claim she had an affair?

16 Which divorced man did Princess Margaret reluctantly decide against marrying in 1955?

17 Which actress was the devoted wife of Humphrey Bogart and nursed him through cancer until his death?

18 Who gave birth to the "love child" of Cabinet minister Cecil Parkinson?

19 Which screen goddess was married (among others) to baseball hero Joe DiMaggio?

20 Which English tennis player did champion Chris Evert marry and divorce?

21 Which two celebrities was actress Mia Farrow married to before her turbulent marriage to Woody Allen?

22 Who married model Victoria Lockwood and admitted sleeping with cartoonist Sally Ann Lasson?

23 Which Cuban-American band leader was married to and starred on television with Lucille Ball?

24 Which Hollywood star had a turbulent relationship with – and married – Richard Burton twice?

25 Defence supremo Sir Peter Harding resigned after the news broke of his affair with whom in 1994?

26 What was the name of the American actress who married Prince Rainier of Monaco?

27 Who married *Die Hard* actor Bruce Willis and appeared nude and pregnant on the cover of *Vanity Fair*?

28 Which beautiful Italian actress did director Carlo Ponti "discover" and marry?

29 With which actor who played James Bond did actress Vanessa Redgrave have a long-standing relationship?

30 To which legendary Hollywood star was "America's sweetheart" Mary Pickford married?

YOU MUST STOP MAKING SNAP JUDGEMENTS.

Answers on page 209

Knowall's question:

What is "The Footsie"?

SOMETHING YOU PLAY !!!

1 Which pop group was known as "The Fab Four"?

2 In politics, who earned the title "The Iron Lady"?

3 Which British institution is nicknamed "Auntie"?

4 In golf, who is "The Golden Bear"?

5 Which American president was "Tricky Dicky"?

6 Name the English actor universally known as "Larry".

7 Which British singer was "Our Gracie"?

8 What British politician was known as "Supermac"?

9 Which quick-fire snooker player is "The Whirlwind"?

10 In cricket, which all-rounder was nicknamed "Beefy"?

11 Which famed hunter and showman was "Buffalo Bill".

12 Which American rock star is "The Boss"?

13 In Grand Prix motor-racing, who was "The Shunt"?

14 Which crooner is nicknamed "Old Blue Eyes"?

15 Who does *Private Eye* satirise as "Brenda"?

16 What Hollywood star was known as "The Duke"?

17 Name the 1930s American gangster called "Scarface".

18 Which rock star is nicknamed "Rubberlips"?

19 Which famous 1990s supermodel is "The Body"?

20 Who were known on TV as "The Two Ronnies"?

21 Which French sex kitten was nicknamed "BB"?

22 Name the Welsh long-jumper called "The Leap".

23 Which ex-soccer playing commentator is "The Saint"?

24 Which World War 2 traitor was "Lord Haw-Haw"?

25 What popular racehorse was nicknamed "Dessie"?

26 Which actor-playwright was "The Master"?

27 Which US tennis player was called "Motormouth"?

28 Which American president is "Billy Blythe"?

29 Who was known as "The King of Swing"?

30 Which centre-forward was "The Lion of Vienna"?

HE'S NEVER HEARD OF STOCKS AND SHARES.

IDIOT

Answers on page 209

Knowall's question:

What kind of animal is a Suffolk Punch?

A SHEEP !!!

1 Which South American country won the first soccer World Cup, held in 1930?

2 What country fielded various "Dream Teams" at the Olympic Games after professionals were admitted?

3 In 1976, who became the first individual to win the Pipesmoker of the Year award for a second time?

4 Name the first German to win the heavyweight boxing championship of the world.

5 For what is the non-complimentary Golden Bull Award given annually?

6 In 1996, what team scored the first-ever "Golden Goal" to win a major international soccer final?

7 Which licensed London taxi driver won the television *Mastermind* title in 1980?

8 *Pulp Fiction* received which prestigious prize at the 1994 Cannes Film Festival?

9 Which English athlete won the men's 100m title at the 1924 Paris Olympics?

10 In 1983, which former winner was the first US skipper ever to *lose* yachting's prestigious America's Cup?

11 Bob Nudd is an English world champion in which popular sport?

12 Who won the World Darts Championship five times between 1980 and 1986?

13 In 1958, which driver was the first Briton ever to win the British Grand Prix outright?

14 Which entomologically-inclined British author won the Nobel Prize for Literature in 1983?

15 In which successive seasons did Liverpool FC win the European Champions Cup?

16 Which organisation presents an annual award for the Cider of the Year?

17 Every decade, what film consistently tops *Sight & Sound* magazine's list of the "Ten Best Films" ever made?

18 Who was the first winner of the Children's Author of the Year Award in 1989?

19 Which professional "oldie" inaugurated a selection of Oldie Awards in 1994?

20 At American Football's annual Superbowl, what do the letters MVP stand for?

21 Apart from Rangers and Celtic, which was the last club to win football's Scottish League Championship?

22 Which contest won by 15-year-old Margaret Gorman was first held in Atlantic City, New Jersey in 1921?

23 In which sport was David Bryant a singles and doubles champion in four decades – from the 1960s to 1990s?

24 Who took the World Chess Championship from Anatoly Karpov in 1985?

25 What coveted viticulture title was secured by Thames Valley Botrytis in 1992?

26 Which county won both cricket's Sunday League and Gillette Cup in 1970?

27 What award has been won by Action Man, Rubik's Cube and Sylvanian Familles?

28 In which competitive field of activity do contestants battle for *The Times*/Knockando Championship?

29 Which English table tennis champion became assistant to racehorse trainer Martin Pipe?

30 Who won a BAFTA Best Actor Award for starring in a hard-hitting psychodrama set in Manchester?

Answers on page 210

Knowall's question:

Who is thought to be the best-selling novelist of all time?

JEFFREY ARCHER !!!

1 Who walked 19,586 miles (31,520km) through four continents and 20 countries between 1983 and 1994?

2 What deeply impressive feat did Jaques Piccard and Don Walsh achieve in the craft *Trieste*?

3 What did Git Kaur Randhawa do at the 48th attempt to drive into the record books?

4 How did Ashrita Furman "travel" for a record 83 miles (133.5km) without actually getting anywhere?

5 Where did Valeriy Poliyakov spend 439 days between 1994 and 1995?

6 How did Michael Stevens survive for 212 hours and 30 minutes in a Royal Navy test tank?

7 Which Japanese production car covered 1,691.6 miles (2,722.3km) on a single tank of petrol?

8 What type of craft flew for a record 18.8 seconds in a New York aircraft hangar?

9 Who was the first man to row in both directions across the Atlantic, taking an aggregate of 191 days?

10 What did Fred E. Magel consume more than 46,000 times over a period of 50 years in 60 countries?

11 Who became the first man to successfully scale all 14 of the world's peaks over 8,000 metres (26,247ft)?

12 What did sailor Laurent Bourgnon complete in a new record of 7 days, 2 hours, 34 minutes and 42 seconds?

13 How did lucky Delores Adams win over $9 million in a Las Vegas casino?

14 In which river did F. P. Newton swim for 1,826 miles (2,939km) over 742 hours in 1930?

15 Who became "the fastest man on Earth" when he ran a 9.84-second 100 metres at the 1996 Olympics?

16 What did Johann Osterrud do for a record 4 hours, 38 minutes between Vancouver and Vanderhoof in 1991?

17 By what means of transport did 46 people from New South Wales manage to travel for over a mile?

18 What did Jackie Bellinger and Lisa Lomas hit to each other a record 173 times in 60 seconds?

19 Which tenor received record applause for 80 minutes through 101 curtain calls at Vienna in 1991?

20 What has Ang Rita Sherpa achieved more times than any other person?

21 Who were the first people to cross the Atlantic Ocean in a hot-air balloon?

22 What did Michael Gavin throw and catch 817 consecutive times to set a record in 1994?

23 In what circumstances did Second Steward Poon Lim survive alone for 133 days in 1942?

24 On what did Akira Matsushima make a 3,260-mile (5,246km) journey from Oregon to Washington D.C.?

25 Who undertook the longest unsupported Antarctic trek from November 1992 to February 1993?

26 What was the record points total achieved in 1995 by a contestant in a heat of *Mastermind*?

27 Fred Lasby became the oldest person to have done what in an aeroplane?

28 In what popular type of car has Albert Klein driven over 1.5 million miles?

29 Using only suction cups and clips, up which building did Daniel Goodwin climb 443.2 metres (713ft)?

30 What did sailors Blake and Knox-Johnston do in a record time of 74 days, 22 hours and 17 minutes?

YOU HAVEN'T GOT A CLUE.

Answers on page 210

Knowall's question:

"Each of his films was the visual equivalent of a great novel." Steven Spielberg talking about which British film director?

KEN RUSSELL !!!

1 "Turn on, tune in, drop out" was the 1967 message from which hippie guru who died in 1996?

2 Which British PM said in 1957: "Let's be frank about it. Most of our people have never had it so good."?

3 Who said to whom many times on screen: "This is another fine mess you've gotten us into."?

4 Which French president inspired French-Canadians on a state visit by pronouncing "Vive le Quebec libre!"?

5 "People can have any colour – so long as it's black." Who said it, and to what was he referring?

6 Which prize-winning author said in 1989: "Frankly, I wish I had written a more critical book."?

7 Which colourful US president's motto for international relations was to "speak softly and carry a big stick"?

8 Who said that if he saw Picasso walking ahead of him down Piccadilly he would "kick him up the arse"?

9 Which American film comedian wrote: "I don't care to belong to any club that will have me as a member."?

10 "The lamps are going out all over Europe." Which British foreign secretary wrote this on 3 August 1914?

11 Which studio boss remarked: "A verbal contract isn't worth the paper it's written on."?

12 Who brandished a meaningless piece of paper at Hendon in 1938 declaring "Peace in our time!"?

13 "Frankly my dear, I don't give a damn." Who said it to whom, and in which film?

14 Who said in 1910: "You see in me the last monarch of the old school."?

15 Which 1960s avant-garde artist claimed that "In the future everyone will be world-famous for 15 minutes."?

16 Which Communist leader thought the truth was that "political power grows out of the barrel of a gun"?

17 "A big hard-boiled city with no more personality than a boiled egg." Raymond Chandler's view of where?

18 Which seductive film actress noted for her one-liners said: "I used to be Snow White but I drifted."?

19 "A week is a long time in politics" – according to which British political leader in 1964?

20 Which diminuitive actor, often in a gangster role, is best remembered for the line: "You dirty rat!"?

21 Which woman critic, reviewing Katherine Hepburn, said: "She ran the whole gamut of emotions from A to B."

22 Which leader talked grandly after World War 1 about creating "a fit country for heroes to live in"?

23 "You're either part of the solution or you're part of the problem" was which radical's slogan of 1968?

24 Which British actor-playwright said: "Never trust a man with short legs – brains too near their bottoms."?

25 Which US President went behind the Iron Curtain to delight West Germans with: "Ich bin ein Berliner!"?

26 What larger-than-life film figure said: "Everything you've ever heard about Hollywood is true – including the lies."?

27 Who spoke the line "That's one small step for a man, one giant leap for mankind," and when?

28 Complete the diary entry: "As always, victory finds a hundred fathers, but defeat is an .... ?

29 Which US president's last words in 1945 were, allegedly, "I have a terrific headache"?

30 What great Hollywood comic actor said: "It's a funny old world – a man's lucky if he gets out of it alive."?

HARDLY. TRY SOMEONE A TAD SLIMMER.

Answers on page 210

QUIZ NUMBER 28

Knowall's question:

In linguistic and social terms, what does PC stand for?

PERSONAL COMPUTER !!!

1 What do the letters QUANGO stand for?

2 Who can be found living in "cardboard city"?

3 What is a "Brixton briefcase"?

4 Who gets swept along by a "Mexican wave"?

5 What does the euphemistic term "friendly fire" mean?

6 In police radio code, what does "IC One" mean?

7 Who or what was the hated BOSS?

8 What do people do through the "Golden Arches"?

9 The military doctrine of MAD involves what madness?

10 A "refuse disposal operative" used to be called what?

11 Who are described as "chronologically challenged"?

12 League soccer linesmen have become what?

13 In secretarial terms, what is WAM?

14 When did Kilroy first start appearing everywhere?

15 In a police interview, who are "Mutt and Jeff"?

16 What is "affirmative action"?

17 "Snow" is a street name for which illegal drug?

18 Which "medics" do image-conscious politicans use?

19 Who gets to occupy a "custody suite"?

20 What was "Reaganomics"?

21 Why is being fitted with a "Denver boot" bad news?

22 What word is conveyed by Charlie Alpha Tango?

23 What are 19.2° E Astra 1A and 23.5° E Kopernikus?

24 In insurance terms, what is an IDS?

25 What is the role of a "pinch hitter" in cricket?

26 Who requires "alternative dentation"?

27 What does a Nimby object to?

28 What do actors contrarily mean by "break a leg"?

29 Who is a "yump"?

30 What is the ZIP in an American ZIP code?

THAT'S NOT THE RIGHT ANSWER.

Answers on page 211

Knowall's question:

Who is Jack Napier's sinister *alter ego*?

THE RIDDLER !!!

1 Who are Mr Fantastic, the Invisible Girl, the Human Torch and the Thing?

2 Who played Batman and sidekick Robin in the long-running 1960s television series?

3 Who is the leader of Marvel's international law enforcement agency, the Avengers?

4 Which *Daily Planet* photographer became Elastic Lad following an accident with a magic potion?

5 Who is the Incredible Hulk, and what is his profession before he transforms into a monster?

6 Which Defender of the Earth is a "master of magic, spells and illusion"?

7 The Lone Ranger's horse is called Silver, but what is the name of Tonto's steed?

8 According to the original American cartoon, who were Spiderman's "amazing friends"?

9 Who is the most continuously published comic-book super-heroine?

10 What is the name of the city in which Judge Dredd administers the law?

11 Name three of the four members of the Teenage Mutant Hero Turtles?

12 Which heroic rodent's catchphrase was "Here I come to save the day"?

13 "The Ghost Who Walks" is the nickname of which environmentally conscious superhero?

14 Which arch cartoon rivals compete for the affections of Olive Oyl?

15 Which maniacal superhero cavorts through the streets of Edge City?

16 Kent Allard, Lamont Cranston and George Clarendon are all aliases for which mysterious crimefighter?

17 Who uses a telekinetically controlled surfboard to travel through air and space at great speed?

18 What is the nature of the relationship between Superman and Supergirl?

19 Who gave British hero SuperTed his powers, and what is the name of his best friend?

20 What colour was the Incredible Hulk when he made his debut in 1962?

21 Name the Olympic swimmer who appeared as Tarzan in a dozen Hollywood films from 1932.

22 Which Marvel character is based on a prominent figure from Norse mythology?

23 Which member of The X-Men has six-foot-long metal claws strong enough to fell a tree?

24 What is Don Diego Vega's secret identity, and what does that name mean?

25 How are secret agents Craig Stirling, Sharon Macready and Richard Barrett collectively known?

26 What is Batgirl's real name, and who is her unsuspecting father?

27 Which scheming criminal is consistently foiled by Superman's amazing powers?

28 In what year did Bob Kane's Batman make his first appearance: 1933, 1939, 1946, 1951 or 1957?

29 Which former "Phantom of the Opera" featured as Condorman in the 1981 Hollywood film of that name?

30 Peter Parker is a daredevil crimefighter by night, but what does he do during the day?

THAT'S A LAUGH.

Answers on page 211

Knowall's question:

Which music megastar narrowly escaped being blown away by a transatlantic "acid bomb" in 1996?

MICHAEL JACKSON !!!

1 What was the name given to the hated British troops sent to Dublin to quell the Irish rebellion in 1919?

2 Which supermarket chain moved to the No. 1 slot in terms of overall sales and profits in 1995?

3 Of which southern state of the USA is Jefferson City the capital?

4 Name the French designer who created the Space Age Collection in 1964.

5 Which part of the body becomes inflamed in those who suffer from gingivitis?

6 In 1964, what did the British colony of Nyasaland become after independence?

7 In which ball sport do countries play for the MacRobertson International Shield?

8 Which soap opera secured a £20-million sponsorship deal from Cadbury?

9 The lead role in *Shirley Valentine* was played by Pauline Collins. Who wrote the story?

10 Which brother of gangsters Ronnie and Reggie was accused of conspiring to supply cocaine?

11 Name the Texas billionaire who ran for president in both 1992 and 1996.

12 Who was the highest paid performer at Woodstock in 1969, appearing for £125,000?

13 What aristocratic title did Anthony-Wedgwood Benn (Tony Benn) relinquish to remain in the Commons?

14 Which three colours appear on the flag of the Republic of Ireland?

15 The Queen was subject to tax for the first time in 1996. Did she pay £1m, £2m, £5m or £10 million?

16 What Allman Brothers tune is used as the theme music for *Top Gear* on both television and radio?

17 Which deposed Asian leader said "I'm fed up with living artificially. I don't want to live like Tito."

18 Witchcraft in which American town was the subject of Arthur Miller's play *The Crucible*?

19 Which group was at No. 1 in the UK singles charts at Christmas 1974 with *Lonely This Christmas?*

20 A world record haul of nearly £3-million worth of what illegal substance was made at Kingston in 1996?

21 Which country won six successive Olympic men's hockey gold medals between 1928 and 1956?

22 What subject did Josef Stalin, dictator of the Soviet Union from 1924 to 1953, study at university?

23 Which is the odd one out: Ursula Andress, Bo Derek, Britt Ekland, Linda Evans?

24 By what name, derived from the original Portuguese colonists, was Taiwan known until the 1960s?

25 Which American comedian's alleged last words were "That's the best ice-cream soda I ever tasted."?

26 Christopher Ewart-Biggs was killed in 1976 when his car was blown up by the IRA. What was his position?

27 Which 1992 Robert Altman film about "Tinseltown" had 65 cameo performances by Hollywood stars?

28 Which dashing fictional World War 1 fighter pilot was created by W. E. Johns?

29 Who played the beleaguered pro-Resistance café owner René in the television series *'Allo 'Allo?*

30 Mary O'Brien is the name of which singer: Vera Lynn, Lulu, Sandie Shaw or Dusty Springfield?

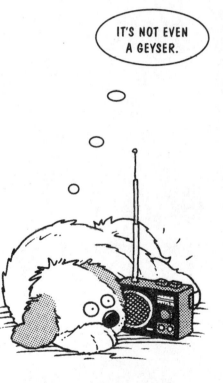

IT'S NOT EVEN A GEYSER.

Answers on page 211

Knowall's question:

Marvin Hamlisch's first Broadway musical ran for 6,137 performances from 1975 to 1990. What was it?

THE SOUND OF MUSIC !!!

1 Which colourful 1960s folk and pop singer's surname is Phillips-Leach?

2 What is the total face value of all the balls on the table at the start of a snooker game?

3 Which European country includes the Transylvanian Alps and has a coastline on the Black Sea?

4 Name one track from *Connected*, other than the title, that made the top 10 for Stereo MCs in 1992-93.

5 Which prime minister of which country held the position for longest for a woman in the 20th century?

6 What is the correct name for an Act of Parliament before it receives the Royal Assent?

7 Which republic consists of over 13,000 islands, including Bali and Timor?

8 What international organisation was set up by the Bretton Woods agreement of 1944?

9 Who is the longest serving member of *The Archers* cast, playing the part of Phil Archer?

10 Which 20th-century head of state is thought to have survived the greatest number of attempts on his life (31)?

11 What was the real first name of the great jazz pianist "Count" Basie?

12 In which European city did the UN General Assembly hold its first meeting, in 1946?

13 Which playwright relative of a prime minister wrote *Lloyd George Knew My Father*?

14 Which ancient monument was sold for £6,000 in 1916 and later presented to the nation?

15 Denis Healey said being questioned by this Tory was like "being savaged by a dead sheep". Which Tory?

16 What was the catchphrase of George Dixon, the PC played by Jack Warner in *Dixon of Dock Green?*

17 Which American motor company introduced the first synchromesh gearbox in 1928?

18 In which year were women first allowed, briefly, into the pavilion at Lord's: 1980, 1984, 1988, 1992, 1996?

19 Who was Britain's first "million pound footballer", moving from Birmingham to Nottingham Forest?

20 The keyboards player with the Charlatans died in a car crash in 1996, aged 29. What was his name?

21 Which aggressive Labour politician is nicknamed "The Beast of Bolsover"?

22 Who was prime minister during both the General Strike of 1926 and the abdication crisis in 1936?

23 Name three of the four musical instruments that make up an orchestra's brass section.

24 Which member of John Major's cabinet has the nickname of "The Ribena Kid" – and why?

25 Walter Swinburn won the Derby on Shergar in 1981. What fate later befell the horse?

26 In 1968 *I'm An Urban Spaceman* provided which inventive group with their only visit to the top 10?

27 Which estranged member of the royal family was governor of the Bahamas during World War 2?

28 In what year did China invade the independent country of Tibet: 1940, 1945, 1950, 1955 or 1960?

29 Which Welshman did Steve Davis defeat to win the 1981 world snooker championship?

30 "Nation shall speak peace unto nation" is the motto of which major British organisation?

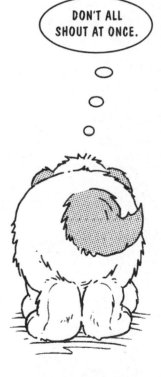

DON'T ALL SHOUT AT ONCE.

Answers on page 211

Knowall's question:

Which ageing pop star had his ninth UK No. 1 single at Christmas in 1993?

PHIL COLLINS!!!

1 Who was the chief witness to the 1979 Camp David agreement between Anwar Sadat and Yasser Arafat?

2 In which 1962 movie did Gregory Peck win an Oscar for his role as a small-town lawyer fighting prejudice?

3 Which previously unsung hero led Leicestershire to cricket's county championship title in 1996?

4 What name is given to the point in the Moon's orbit where it is closest to the Earth?

5 What Japanese word describes the action of a pilot who deliberately crashes his plane?

6 At which English racecourse does the annual "Festival of National Hunt Racing" take place?

7 "The Great White Way" is another name for which famous New York thoroughfare?

8 Which television actor played both a time-travelling doctor and a chaotic vet?

9 British composer Michael Nyman scored the music for which 1993 Oscar-winning movie set in New Zealand?

10 Which player with an East Anglian club moved north to become Britain's first £5 million footballer in 1994?

11 What is the name of an optical illusion caused by the atmospheric conditions?

12 Which Scottish athletics event involves carrying a vertical pole and throwing it forward?

13 In what year did Congress give American Indians the rights of US citizens: 1904, 1909, 1914, 1919, 1924?

14 Which fabric beloved of cowboys and young people is named after the French fabric *serge de Nîmes*?

15 By what acronym is the International Association of Poets, Playwrights, Editors and Novelists known?

16 In 1985, which Japanese firm introduced the first body-integrated autofocus single-lens reflex camera?

17 Which writer and poet's last words are alleged to be: "I'm dying as I lived – beyond my means."?

18 Name the lyricist who collaborated with Frederick Loewe on the musicals *My Fair Lady* and *Camelot*.

19 What did the French physicist Charles Fabry identify in the upper atmosphere in 1913?

20 In the 1972 Olympics who beat the USA 51-50 in the last second to inflict a historic basketball defeat?

21 Which renowned orchestral conductor was known to his professional contemporaries as "Flash Harry"?

22 In which nation, war-torn for six years, did a peaceful general election take place on 14 September 1996?

23 Why did mountaineers Dougal Haston and Doug Scott have reason to celebrate in 1976?

24 The Hermitage Museum houses one of Europe's finest collections. In which Russian city is it located?

25 The first volume of which English actor's autobiography was called *The Moon's A Balloon*?

26 General Zia ul-Haq was blown up in an aircraft in 1988. Of which country was he the president?

27 At which English ground was the world's first six-figure football crowd (114,815) recorded in 1901?

28 Under what pseudonym did Sir William Connor write for many years in the *Daily Mirror*?

29 What was Ghana before it became the first colonial African country to secure independence in 1957?

30 Which two other countries joined the EEC at the same time as Great Britain?

NICE ONE, SIR.

Answers on page 212

Knowall's question:

What was the name of Sony's first personal stereo?

THE GHETTO-BLASTER !!!

1 In the 1940s, which weapon was constructed under the supervision of Robert Oppenheimer?

2 What is the name given to devices used to convert radio waves into electric signals?

3 What valuable aeronautical aid was invented by the American Elmer Sperry in 1913?

4 Which inert gas is used in the majority of modern fire extinguishers?

5 What useful kitchen appliance is associated with the name of inventor Charles Strite?

6 Of what could the powerful microscope developed by Max Kroll and Ernst Ruska in 1933 produce an image?

7 Which German company introduced the first plastic audio cassette tape?

8 What unconscious contribution did Erik Rotheim make to future global warming in 1926?

9 Where in England did the world's first radio telescope go into operation?

10 Why is the name of William Taynton familiar to experts on the history of television?

11 What nickname did Hubert Booth's 1901 fuel-driven vacuum cleaner share with a 19th-century locomotive?

12 Philip Drinker contributed the respirator to medical technology. By what alternative name is it known?

13 By what title did America's Strategic Defence Initiative become universally known?

14 In 1901, who sent the first radio signal across the Atlantic in morse code?

15 What was significant about the Soviet ice-breaker *Lenin*, which made its maiden voyage in 1959?

16 What loud contribution to popular culture was made by Rickenbacker, Barth and Beauchamp in 1931?

17 Why might chemist Fritz Haber be seen as both hero and villain of World War 1 weapons technology?

18 What communications advance did Telstar make possible from 1962?

19 Who invented a hand-held device capable of detecting radiation in 1908?

20 For what mode of transport is Christopher Cockerell largely responsible?

21 The wife of a British monarch used an early hearing aid invented by Miller Reese Hutchinson. Who was she?

22 What is the name of the gas used to cool the contents of a refrigerator?

23 What was the approximate range of Germany's World War 2 rocket weapon, the V-2?

24 Which American company produced the world's first word processor?

25 Which of Robert Watson-Watt's inventions underpinned Britain's air defences during World War 2?

26 In which year was the facsimile machine invented: 1907, 1928, 1940, 1961, 1974?

27 Waldemar Poulsen's machine the "Telegraphon" was an early example of what?

28 What contribution did Peter Goldmark make to future viewing pleasure in 1940?

29 How did James Martin make the life of military pilots safer after World War 2?

30 In which decade did Chester Carlson invent the photocopier: 1920s, 1930s, 1940s, 1950s, 1960s?

TIME FOR A STROLL.

Answers on page 212

Knowall's question:

In 1900, what Herbert Short invention amplified the future of sound?

THE HEARING AID !!!

1 What does an electrocardiograph machine monitor?

2 Who was the first man to build a nuclear reactor?

3 Of what was ENIAC an early example?

4 What firm introduced waterproof watches in 1927?

5 Which element is vital to manufacturing microchips?

6 What did Robert Goddard launch in 1926?

7 How did C. C. Magee incur the wrath of drivers in 1932?

8 How is the positive electrode of a battery also known?

9 "Electric Shadows" is the Chinese name for what?

10 What revolutionised radio listening from 1948?

11 The computer term BIT is an abbreviation of what?

12 What 1945 Percy Spencer patent transformed cooking?

13 The degeneration of a reactor's core is called what?

14 How did Eugene Schueller help sun-seekers from 1936?

15 What city first had more than one television channel?

16 What is the meaning of DERV?

17 What did Philips and Sony pioneer in 1979?

18 In 1912, Charles Kettering invented what motoring aid?

19 Which type of clock is the most accurate?

20 What does HDTV stand for?

21 Of what is Fermilab an example?

22 *Echo* and *Courier* were America's first what in 1960?

23 Who first vulcanised rubber in 1939?

24 What cooking aid did Marc Grégoir devise in 1954?

25 How did Louis and Jacques Breguet achieve lift-off?

26 What new material did Courtaulds introduce in 1964?

27 What "anti-bends" aid for divers was introduced in 1929?

28 In which country was the automatic gearbox invented?

29 James Ransome's claim to gardening fame is what?

30 What power cut did Jacob Schick make possible?

YOU'RE SPEAKING LOUD AND CLEAR.

Answers on page 212

Knowall's question:

What American edifice has two towers, 99 lifts and more office space than any other building in the world?

THE SEARS TOWER !!!

EASY

1 In which European country is the world's longest road tunnel located?

2 What is the name of the ingenious structure designed to protect London from flooding?

3 What is the 800-mile (1,287km) TAPS, completed in May 1977 at a cost of $8 billion?

4 How is the complex Gravelly Hill Interchange north of Birmingham popularly known?

5 Name the world's then-longest suspension bridge, completed in 1931 to link Manhattan and New Jersey.

6 Which London landmark was designed by US architect Cesar Pelli and topped off in November 1990?

7 What was the engineering significance of the meeting between Graham Fagg and Philipe Cozette in 1990?

8 In which London arts and residential complex is the Shakespeare Tower, Britain's tallest block of flats?

9 Name the enclosed, self-sufficient environment in which eight people lived from 1991 to 1993.

10 What flows through the complex network built under the Chicago Tunnels and Reservoirs Plan?

11 Which telescope was launched into space in 1990 to study the origins of the Universe?

12 The Ultimate, Steel Phantom and Desperado are all types of what?

13 Which London Underground line is being extended to service Docklands?

14 Which dam, replacing an earlier structure, was finished in 1971 to control the flood level of the Nile?

15 Name the world's then-longest underwater tunnel, completed in England at a cost of £7 million in 1932.

16 Which indoor arena is covered by the world's largest retractable roof?

17 The world's longest rail tunnel links two islands in which country?

18 Which estuary is crossed by a new bridge on the M4 motorway, completed in 1996?

19 In 1993 at Cape Tarifa, Europe's largest wind-powered energy generator came on line in which country?

20 The Quai Herman du Pasquier in Le Havre is the world's biggest example of what?

21 Name the two American space probes which landed on Mars in 1976 to gather data on the "Red Planet".

22 Which road extends for 15,000 miles (24,000km) between Chile and Alaska?

23 What New York landmark stands on the site of the former Waldorf-Astoria Hotel?

24 Which Brazilian football stadium has a capacity of over 200,000 spectators?

25 The world's tallest structure at 646m (2,120ft) collapsed in 1991. In which country was it located?

26 What became Britain's longest span cable suspension bridge on its completion in 1996?

27 What did the massive Madina and Al-Jabail Al-Sinaiyah construction project in Saudi Arabia create?

28 In which Texas city is the spectacular 750ft (229m) Tower of the Americas?

29 What is the name of the last nuclear power station to be completed in Britain?

30 Which impressive bridge has guarded the entrance to San Francisco Bay since 1937?

HE'S NEVER THOUGHT OF TRADING PLACES.

Answers on page 213

QUIZ NUMBER 36

Knowall's question:

Who now owns the Aston Martin car company?

MERCEDES !!!

1. The Italian Countach and Diablo are models of which expensive sports car?

2. In America, for what purpose was the massive Marion eight-caterpillar crawler transport designed?

3. Which Rolls-Royce model is the most popular ever to have been produced?

4. Three Jaguar engines, 15,600cc, 24ft (7.3m) long, theoretical top speed 360mph (580km/h). What is it?

5. In what early Steven Spielberg film is an unfortunate motorist pursued by a sinister petrol tanker?

6. Which used car fetched a staggering £6,410,000 at a Sotheby's auction in 1990?

7. What speed record did Robert E. Barber set in the car *Steamin' Demon* at 145.6mph (234.33km/h)?

8. What is the name of the most powerful and expensive car in standard production?

9. General Motors produce an impressive vehicle called the Terex Titan. What is it?

10. In 1983, the jet car *Thrust 2* covered a mile in a record: 4.8, 5.7, 6.9, 7.3 or 8.1 seconds?

11. Which German airship returned to New Jersey in 1929 after circumnavigating the globe in 21 days?

12. *Half-Safe* circumnavigated the globe in 1958. What was unusal about the feat?

13. What circumnavigated the globe in just nine days on a single tank of fuel in 1986?

14. In the film *Goldeneye*, which manufacturer built the car driven by James Bond?

15. What is the nickname of the plane that holds the official airspeed record of 2,193.17mph (3,529.47km/h)?

16 In the books by Colin Dexter, what car did Inspector Morse drive before TV put him in a Jaguar Mk II?

17 How was Grey Gabelich's car *Blue Flame* propelled to speeds in excess of 630mph (1,014km/h)?

18 Automotively, for what is rural Hethel near Norwich in Norfolk known?

19 Before the end of the Cold War, in what make of large black car were Soviet leaders always seen?

20 The price is massive, it can do 348km/h (217mph) and many customers tried to avoid delivery. What is it?

21 The American Stealth bomber which is invisible to radar carries what identification code?

22 What do the letters GT stand for when used as part of a car's name or description?

23 Who formed a new Grand Prix racing team for 1997, with Ford engines and banking sponsorship?

24 What is the special distinction of the Jaguar XJ12 Chubb Firefighter?

25 Which British truck manufacturer produced a "zoo" which included the Lynx, Hippo, Lion and Octopus?

26 Of the many pre-war motor cars produced by the Bugatti company, which was the most luxurious?

27 Name the two American manufacturers of classic V-twin motorcycles.

28 Which classic British sports car returned to the road after an absence with the "F" model?

29 What feat have Cesare Fiorio and the crew of the *Destriero* achieved more swiftly than anybody else?

30 Which Formula 1 team did world champion Michael Schumacher join for the 1996 season?

HE CAN'T AFFORD ONE ANYWAY.

Answers on page 213

Knowall's question:

In 1915, what sociable practice was banned in Britain with a £100 fine for offenders?

KISSING !!!

1 The Kaiser declared war on the Czar on 1 August 1914. How were they related?

2 Which two Norfolk towns were the first British targets of Zeppelin raids in World War 1?

3 In May 1916, the "greatest naval battle in history" ended in stalemate. Where?

4 From what range did the German heavy gun "Big Bertha" shell Paris, killing hundreds of civilians?

5 In 1914, which former president criticised America's attitude to the war as "tame and spiritless neutrality"?

6 What peninsula did Allied troops invade in 1915 against fierce Turkish resistance?

7 Which feature of a British spring that remains to this day was first introduced in 1916?

8 In 1917, all of which country's nationals were detained in Germany as hostages?

9 Who replaced Sir John French as commander of British forces on the Western Front in December 1915?

10 What notable "first" did French aviator Captain Sarret achieve in July 1918?

11 Which Middle Eastern city was captured by General Allenby's forces in December 1917?

12 The first German bomb of World War 1 fell on London in: 1914, 1915, 1916, 1917, 1918?

13 What German colony in Africa was occupied by the Allies in January 1916?

14 At what age did British children leave school after the leaving age was changed in 1918?

15 Germany's enemies were the Allies, but what was the collective name for Germany and its friends?

16 What rotary-engined British fighter aircraft was known for drenching pilots with burned oil?

17 It has been known as Asian flu, Chinese flu and more besides. What was it called in the epidemic of 1918?

18 Which country's planes mounted an attack on Venice in May 1915?

19 Who became Chief of the German General Staff in August 1917?

20 In what month of 1918 did the Allies finally break through the German lines in France?

21 It was launched by American car-maker Henry Ford in 1918, but what exactly was the *Eagle*?

22 At which river did Allied troops stem the German advance on Paris in September 1914?

23 What did Saxe-Coburg-Gotha and Battenberg become in June 1917?

24 Which country was the first to recognise Russia's revolutionary government in 1917?

25 What merged with the Royal Naval Air Service in 1918 to form the Royal Air Force?

26 How many British warships (including auxilliaries) were sunk in World War 1: 397, 565, 798, 1,069, 1,281?

27 Where were Czar Nicholas II and his family murdered in July 1918?

28 Who was in command of the American Expeditionary Force in Europe?

29 In Jan 1916, the UK female workforce had grown in a year by: 50,000, 250,000, 1 million or 2 million?

30 Name the defensive fortifications to which the Germans withdrew in France during November 1917.

THE DRINKS ARE ON HIM.

Answers on page 213

Knowall's question:

What were well-off families asked to dispense with in 1916 to help the war effort?

THEIR IRON RAILINGS !!!

1 In August 1914, Britain honoured the Treaty of London (1839). What did the treaty guarantee?

2 Against considerable opposition in the country, what was voted in by parliament in January 1916?

3 On what Greek island is that "corner of a foreign field that is forever England" where poet Rupert Brooke lies?

4 In 1916, what major new weapon did the Allies deploy in France, but in insufficient numbers for great effect?

5 Who became prime minister of Russia in July 1917 and pledged to continue the war against Germany?

6 British troops claimed to have seen a vision of an angel when retreating from which Belgian town in 1914?

7 How close did the great German offensive of 1918 with troops from the Eastern Front come to Paris?

8 Where did Russia's Bolshevik government sign a humiliating peace treaty with Germany in 1918?

9 In 1915, who publicly offered to abstain from drinking alcohol to set an example to war workers?

10 In 1917, the first American troops reached France on: 17 April, 17 June, 17 August, 17 October?

11 Which dancer with a name meaning "eye of the morning" was executed as a German spy in Paris?

12 Where in the South Atlantic did the Royal Navy win a sea battle at the end of 1914?

13 Who did the Germans return to Russia in a sealed train in April 1917?

14 Asquith, Balfour, Kitchener, Bonar Law, Lloyd George, McKenna. How were they collectively known in 1915?

15 With which country did Russia refuse to sign an armistice in April 1916?

16 Who became the British prime minister in December 1916, replacing Herbert Asquith?

17 Name one of the four east coast towns shelled by the German navy in December 1914.

18 Who led Arab horsemen into Damascus in October 1918 after fighting the Turks all the way from Arabia?

19 Which Frenchman accepted the German surrender on behalf of the Allies in 1918?

20 What ruse used to protect British shipping angered American President Woodrow Wilson in 1915?

21 German fighter ace Manfred von Richthofen was killed in 1918. What was his nickname?

22 How many British and Empire military casualties were there in the Great War: 1, 2, 3, 4 or 5 million?

23 What terrible new weapon was first used by the Germans north of Ypres in April 1915?

24 In which country did "Kaiser Bill" seek refuge after his abdication in 1918?

25 Name the British secretary for war who died when the cruiser HMS *Hampshire* hit a mine in June 1916.

26 What new technique did Britain employ to protect merchant shipping from U-boat attacks from 1917?

27 Germany's last serious offensive of the war was called *Friedensturm*. What is the literal translation?

28 A massive Allied attack began on which river in Picardy during July 1916?

29 At what symmetrical time and date did the Armistice effectively end the European war?

30 Which treaty, finally signed in June 1919, formally ended World War 1?

HE HASN'T GOT MUCH DOWNSTAIRS.

Answers on page 213

Knowall's question:

Who said the Labour party would "fall back on some sort of Gestapo" if elected in 1945?

HEINRICH HIMMLER !!!

1 On what date in 1939 did Great Britain declare war on Germany?

2 Following the German invasion in 1941, to what aptly-named site was Russian tank production relocated?

3 Which two aircraft formed the backbone of the RAF's Fighter Command during the Battle of Britain?

4 On what well-remembered date did "Operation Overlord" get under way in 1944?

5 What Benedictine monastery in Italy became a German stronghold that delayed the Allies in 1943?

6 In October 1939, which British battlehip was torpedoed and sunk in Scapa Flow?

7 How many POWs were executed following the "Great Escape" from Stalag Luft III in 1944: 17, 29, 35, 47?

8 What great British naval base and "impregnable fortress" fell to the Japanese in February 1942?

9 In October 1944, who fulfilled a promise by returning to the Philippines at the head of his American troops?

10 Which German force under General Rommel arrived in North Africa in 1941 to bolster Italian resistance?

11 In March 1945, the Allies crossed the Rhine using which bridge that the Germans had failed to destroy?

12 How old was Adolf Hitler when he died on 30 April 1945: 51, 56, 59, 63 or 66?

13 Which former inmate of a Manchester lunatic asylum was chosen by Hitler as his successor?

14 What bitterly fought if short northern war ended on 13 March 1940?

15 At which naval base was the French fleet scuttled as German panzers approached in November 1942?

16 Germany's rocket weapon was universally known as the V-2, but what was its official military designation?

17 In July 1943, where did the great tank battle that broke Germany's hold on the Eastern Front take place?

18 On 7 May 1945, where did Germany surrender unconditionally to end the war in Europe?

19 Roughly how many people are thought to have died in World War 2: 17, 31, 43, 55 or 62 million?

20 Poland was invaded with very little warning on 30 September 1939. By whom?

21 The "bloodiest land fighting of the Pacific War" ended with America's capture of what island in June 1945?

22 In July 1942, at which battle was the German advance in North Africa halted?

23 In December 1943, who was appointed Allied supreme commander for the invasion of Western Europe?

24 In 1940, who was asassinated with an ice pick by Russian agents in Mexico City?

25 What did the Lancaster bombers of Guy Gibson's 617 Squadron achieve in May 1943?

26 Which British force once numbering 1,084 battalions was disbanded in November 1944?

27 What was significant about the fate of the destroyer USS *Reuben James* in October 1941?

28 What was the name of Germany's twin-engined jet fighter-bomber aircraft which saw action in 1944-45?

29 Britain's standard light machine-gun in World War 2 was named after which two arms manufacturing towns?

30 What was particularly humiliating about the location where France surrendered to Germany in 1940?

DON'T SAY THAT IN CHURCH.

Answers on page 214

Knowall's question:

Which great European capital was "liberated" by the Russians in April 1945 with all its great buildings intact?

BERLIN !!!

1 "Operation Dynamo" was the code name of which hazardous troop movement?

2 In August 1942, where in France did Allied troops mount a daring raid on Hitler's "Fortress Europe"?

3 What was the dreaded indication that a German V-1 "doodlebug" flying bomb was about to fall?

4 In 1944, Germany's young, old, lame and sick were conscripted into which defence force?

5 What was the only part of the United Kingdom to be occupied by German troops in World War 2?

6 On 13 October 1943, which country surprisingly declared war on Germany?

7 SS troops slaughtered 50,000 Jewish people in what East European ghetto in September 1942?

8 Complete the sequence of D-Day beaches: Utah, Omaha, Gold, Juno and .... ?

9 Which organisation sprang from a July 1942 gathering at a Quaker meeting house in Oxford?

10 What was unusual about the George Cross which was awarded on 16 April 1942?

11 Name the flamboyant American general whose tanks burst into Germany's Saar Basin in November 1944.

12 In August 1943, Allied bombers attacked which German rocket base in the Baltic?

13 Mistakes made at a high level led to the almost total destruction of PQ-17 in 1942. What was PQ-17?

14 In April 1943, what grisly discovery did German troops make in a forest at Katyn near Smolensk?

15 Where on the Rhine did an ambitious airborne Allied operation end in bloody failure in September 1944?

16 Which British traitor was shot in the thigh and captured on the Danish border in June 1945?

17 Which country's troops led the Allied invasion of Vichy-French North Africa in November 1942?

18 Italian dictator Benito Mussolini and Clara Petacci were shot by partisans in April 1945. Who was she?

19 Which robust Russian tank was largely responsible for German's ultimate defeat on the Eastern Front?

20 In 1943, Britain's "Bevin Boys" were called up to work in which industry?

21 Which popular British author broadcast from Germany to America in 1941 and was branded as a traitor?

22 The long German siege of which town ended with the surrender of Field Marshal von Paulus in 1943?

23 What was the cruel irony when U-156 sank the British transport ship *Laconia* with massive loss of life?

24 With whom did Britain sign a 20-year "treaty of alliance and mutual assistance" in 1942?

25 In 1945, what name was claimed by fanatical Nazis who harried the Allies in occupied Germany?

26 In Chicago, atomic energy became reality with a controlled chain reaction in: 1942, 1943, 1944, 1945?

27 Name the British aircraft carrier torpedoed by an Italian submarine off Gibraltar in November 1941.

28 Which important royal died on active service when a flying-boat crashed on the way to Iceland in 1942?

29 What international Communist organisation founded in 1919 was dissolved by Stalin in 1943?

30 In 1945, a classic photograph showed four American Marines raising the flag on which Pacific island?

I SUPPOSE THEY JUST WALTZED IN.

Answers on page 214

Knowall's question:

Which country was finally defeated in Vietnam at the battle of Dien Bien Phu?

THE USA !!!

1. What type of missile did Iraq fire at Saudi Arabia and Israel during the Gulf War?

2. Which country invaded South Korea in 1950, thus precipitating the Korean War?

3. Who assumed command of British forces in the Boer War in January 1900?

4. What event caused an abortive invasion of Egypt by British, French and Israeli troops in 1956?

5. Which two countries went to war over Kashmir in September 1965?

6. Who was the governor of the Falkland Islands when Argentina invaded them?

7. In which European country did a savage civil war flare up in June 1991?

8. How many Allied coalition troops died in the Gulf War: 192, 265, 301, 344, 393?

9. In the Korean War, "Operation Chromite" involved a daring UN amphibious landing at which port?

10. Who was the leader of the Kenyan guerillas in their successful war against British rule?

11. Attack. Advance. Capture Jerusalem. Victory. Nasser falls. Cease-fire. Which war?

12. How many Argentinian troops were killed during their invasion of the Falklands in April 1982?

13. In which country did Contra rebels, with CIA support, fight the Sandinista government in the 1980s?

14. In 1905, war broke out when Japanese torpedo boats attacked which country's fleet at Port Arthur?

15. In 1965, which president committed the first American ground troops used in Vietnam?

16 Which Asian country was invaded by the Soviet army in December 1979?

17 What was the code name of the military operation mounted to recover Kuwait from Iraq in 1992?

18 An Italian assault on Tripoli in 1911 started a brief but intense war with which country?

19 In April 1982, which island did Royal Marines recapture three weeks after it was occupied by Argentina?

20 In South-east Asia, a vicious border war broke out between which two countries in February 1979?

21 Which missile was used to devastating effect against British ships in the Falklands War?

22 Name the Vietcong offensive that hit the heart of Saigon in January 1968.

23 What "war" officially ended on 3 December 1989 at a shipboard meeting off Malta?

24 Which city called "the pearl of the Adriatic" was besieged and badly damaged in October 1991?

25 Name the British officer who won a posthumous Victoria Cross at the Battle of Goose Green.

26 What country took advantage of China's internal strife to invade the country in 1932?

27 Where was the dividing line between North and South established at the end of the Korean War?

28 How long did the lightning ground action which ended the Gulf War last: 80, 100, 120, 140 or 160 hours?

29 In what year did the Vietnam War end with the panic evacuation of the American embassy in Saigon?

30 At what US air base was a peace accord aimed at ending the Bosnian conflict reached?

HE'S GOT A FROG IN HIS THROAT.

Answers on page 214

Knowall's question:

Who became president of Kenya in 1993 after the country's first multi-party elections?

JOMO KENYATTA !!!

1 On which island in Table Bay, off Cape Town, was Nelson Mandela imprisoned for 18 years?

2 Mohammad Ali Jinnah was the "founding father" and first president of which Asian country in 1947?

3 The Nationalsozialistiche Deutsche Arbeiterpartei were better known by what name?

4 Which vociferous cleric came to prominence as the leader of Ulster's Democratic Unionist Party?

5 Churchill, Roosevelt and Stalin met twice, in 1943 and 1945. Name one of the two venues.

6 Who said in 1995: "What we have done for Paris we will do for France."?

7 Which country invaded and occupied East Timor after the Portuguese left the island in 1975?

8 Which two leaders signed the first SALT (Strategic Arms Limitation Talks) treaty in 1974?

9 Moise Tshombe led the breakaway of Katanga province in 1960. From which African country?

10 Which "lady" leader of Westminster Council was accused of "gerrymandering" to Torify her area?

11 In which year did Benito Mussolini seize power in Italy: 1922, 1926, 1930, 1934, 1938?

12 In 1991, which were the first two Yugoslavian republics to declare themselves independent?

13 South Africa's Inkatha Freedom Party consists largely of members from which tribe?

14 What links King Faisal of Saudi Arabia, President Sadat of Egypt and Prime Minister Rabin of Israel?

15 Pierre Trudeau was prime minister of which country twice between 1968 and 1984?

16 Who comes next: Trigvie Lie, Dag Hammarskjöld, U Thant, Kurt Waldheim, Javier Pérez de Cuellar?

17 Which Australian tycoon won the America's Cup in 1983 – and was convicted of fraud in 1996?

18 Which Bolshevik newspaper, later the mouthpiece of the Soviet government, was founded in 1912?

19 Who was the leader of Czechoslovakia during the brief 1968 attempt to resist Soviet domination?

20 Which South American leader ruled from 1946, was exiled in 1955, returned in 1973 but died in 1974?

21 Which nation was the United Kingdom's foe in the so-called "Cod Wars" of 1958 and 1975?

22 In what year did the Soviet Union send tanks into Budapest to quell the Hungarian uprising?

23 What Republican candidate was annihilated by Lyndon Johnson in the presidential election of 1964?

24 Which South Pacific island, independent since 1970, is still ruled as a feudal monarchy by Taufa'ahau Tupou II?

25 Which two neighbouring countries fought the "first" Gulf War between 1980 and 1988?

26 The Treaty of Portsmouth (1905) marked the military defeat and humiliation of which country by Japan?

27 Name the resilient Irishman who was prime minister of the Republic three times between 1979 and 1992.

28 Which European country withdrew their forces from NATO command in 1974?

29 Which former Swedish premier became the main peacemaker in the Bosnian War of the early 1990s?

30 What European country, independent since 1291, is divided into 23 powerful cantons?

INTO THE LION'S DEN

Answers on page 215

Knowall's question:

Who toppled President Batista in 1959?

THE AMERICANS !!!

1 In which city were the headquarters of the United Nations established in 1945?

2 Edith Cresson became the first woman president of which Western European country in 1991?

3 Who was the father of Indira Gandhi, twice prime minister of India until her assassination in 1984?

4 For what illuminating act in 1933 is a deranged Dutch ex-Communist Marinus van der Lubbe known?

5 Which "murderous priest" was exiled to the Seychelles by the British authorities in 1956?

6 Jan Smuts was prime minister of which African country from 1919 to 1924 and 1939 to 1948?

7 Rasputin, Russia's "Mad Monk", was the favourite of which tsar who was murdered by revolutionaries?

8 In which unlikely city does OPEC (Organisation of Petroleum Exporting Countries) have its HQ?

9 Which Indian leader was described by Churchill as a "seditious and half-naked fakir" in 1935?

10 The "Shining Path" is the Marxist terrorist group in which South American country?

11 Who was the inaugural president of Ghana, first African nation to become independent of Britain?

12 What is the guerrilla organisation that forced the Soviet Union to withdraw from Afghanistan in 1989?

13 Which North African country is divided into 25 administrative areas called "governorates"?

14 Name the modern "war hero" who resisted pressure from the Republicans to run for president in 1996.

15 Who was the Romanian dictator whose neo-Stalinist 25-year rule was ended with his execution in 1989?

16 Which notorious Asian president's wife was famous for her vast collection of shoes?

17 Name the Australian prime minister who was in office first in 1939-41 and then for 17 years from 1949.

18 What triggered the brief war between neighbours El Salvador and Honduras in 1969?

19 On whose behalf have ETA (Euskadi ta Askatasuna) conducted a terrorist bomb campaign since 1968?

20 Franjo Tudjman became president of which newly independent Eastern European nation in 1991?

21 Which strife-ridden Caribbean country elected Father Aristide as its first democratic president in 1990?

22 The "velvet revolution" is the name given to the transition from Communism to capitalism in which country?

23 Which former terrorist, head of the extremist Irgun group, became Prime Minister of Israel in 1977?

24 What internationally agreed "rules of war" drawn up in 1864 were revised in 1906, 1929, 1949 and 1977?

25 Which Iraqi leader took on the world by invading Kuwait but retained power despite crushing defeat?

26 Which renowned French novelist was a cabinet minister in the government of Charles de Gaulle?

27 David Lange was the prime minister of which Commonwealth country from 1984 to 1989?

28 Who is *not* a member of G7: Canada, China, France, Germany, Italy, Japan, UK, USA?

29 Which British monarch instructed "No more coals to Newcastle, no more Hoares to Paris. ?

30 Which Australian prime minister was accused of "manhandling" the Queen on a state visit?

FAITHFUL TO THE LAST.

Answers on page 215

Knowall's question:

Which British free-skater won a gold medal at the 1976 Winter Olympics?

CHRISTOPHER DEAN !!!

1 Every year there are spectacular autumn illuminations along which British resort's "Golden Mile"?

2 A motor-cycle with an engine capacity of less than 50cc is generally known as what?

3 Which "Grand Old Woman of Israeli politics" became the country's prime minister in 1969?

4 In what Dean Martin-Jerry Lewis comedy did moody screen idol James Dean make his film debut?

5 Where would the new country of "Padania" appear if the Northern League political party had its way?

6 By what name is a test carried out with a polygraph more commonly known?

7 Which two countries contested cricket's first-ever World Cup final in 1975?

8 Name the "silent" member of the Marx Brothers, who never spoke on film.

9 Egypt's surprise attack on Israel and the subsequent fighting in 1973 became known as what war?

10 Chris Bonington made his reputation in the 1960s and 1970s undertaking what strenuous activity?

11 In computer terminology, what does the acronym WYSIWYG mean?

12 In which year was the first motorway opened in Britain: 1955, 1959, 1963, 1967, 1971?

13 In which South African township did police massacre 56 inhabitants and injure hundreds in 1960?

14 Who wrote the classic children's book *Charlie and the Chocolate Factory*?

15 In 1983, which prominent former actress and well-known wife died in a car crash in the south of France?

16 In 1964, what was the name of the first "pirate" radio to broadcast pop music to Britain?

17 What is the British Army's equivalent rank to the Royal Air Force's flight lieutenant?

18 How long after the end of World War 1 did League football recommence: 2, 12, 22, 32, 42, 52 days?

19 Between which two cities do members of the European Parliament commute regularly for sittings?

20 Which barefoot South African distance runner was given rapid dispensation to run for Britain in 1984?

21 In which year did Queen Elizabeth II celebrate her silver jubilee?

22 In 1980, which tough-guy actor died of cancer in Mexico just after marrying his 25-year-old third wife?

23 In what year did Coca-Cola introduce its distinctive contoured bottle: 1909, 1916, 1923, 1931?

24 Which spiritual Christian leader died in 1978 after only 33 days in office?

25 Which oriental film detective has been variously played by J. Carrol Naish, Warner Oland and Peter Ustinov?

26 What nickname is given to someone who sells shares in the hope of buying them back later at a lower price?

27 In what year did the Concorde airliner enter scheduled passenger service: 1968, 1972, 1976, 1980, 1984?

28 At which London Underground station did a fire kill 30 people in 1987?

29 The TV sensation of 1963 was satirical show *That Was The Week That Was*. What was its nickname?

30 The wife of a murdered opposition leader forced President Marcos to abdicate in 1986. Who is she?

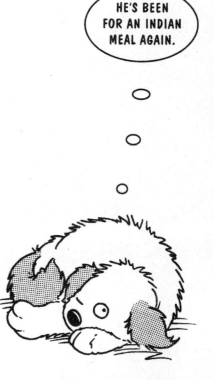

HE'S BEEN FOR AN INDIAN MEAL AGAIN.

Answers on page 215

Knowall's question:

How did the novelist Virginia Woolf die?

OF HEART FAILURE !!!

1 Who became the manager of Liverpool FC in 1959?

2 On film, what was action-man Rambo's first name?

3 What is the link between Lanzarote and Tenerife?

4 Who was known as "il Duce"?

5 What do the initials CND stand for?

6 Which Beatle made the solo album *Extra Texture*?

7 Who is odd man out: Alfie, Harvey, Oscar, Tommy?

8 Name the longest river in Scotland.

9 Who captained Holland in the 1974 World Cup final?

10 Which human organ is affected by nephritis?

11 Who was the first British cricketer to be knighted?

12 What was South Africa's post-1948 racial policy?

13 Which pirate film lost Carolco Pictures £70 million?

14 What is the horse racing season's final "classic" race?

15 Who became chancellor of West Germany in 1982?

16 How many players are there in a netball team?

17 What viral illness is named after a Nigerian village?

18 OCR stands for what in computer terminology?

19 Which political party did James Goldsmith form in 1994?

20 What sort of creature is the original mugger?

21 Which ragtime pianist wrote *The Entertainer*?

22 What are stabilisers, enhancers and emulsifiers?

23 The phrase "Habemus Papam" signifies what?

24 What discipline was started by Maharishi Mahesh Yogi?

25 Which East London flats partially collapsed in 1968?

26 What is the British actors' union called?

27 Jim Dixon was the comic hero of which novel?

28 By what title are the world's wealthiest nations known?

29 Which legendary American comedian lived to be 100?

30 Lilongwe is the capital of which African country?

I GET THAT SINKING FEELING.

Answers on page 215

QUIZ NUMBER 46

Knowall's question:

In which country is the airline Qantas based?

QATAR !!!

1 In what "Top 10" may Angel, Ribbon and Pilao be found?

2 What sort of creature is a firebrat?

3 Which type of plants are studied by mycologists?

4 In what year did Heathrow Airport open to passengers?

5 Who plays F. W. de Klerk on film in *One Man One Vote*?

6 Which "super" gas is represented by the symbol *Kr*?

7 *Adi Granth* are sacred scriptures of which religion?

8 What connects gin, salmon and Barbara Cartland?

9 What do the initials RNLI stand for?

10 In geometry, what measure is a 60th of a degree?

11 The savoy is a variety of what vegetable?

12 To what insect does the adjective formic relate?

13 Which famous escapologist was born Erich Weiss?

14 The sackbut was an old name for which instrument?

15 Which recent American president was called "Dutch"?

16 Name the fibrous tissue that attaches bones at a joint.

17 Which British novelist wrote *The Plague Dogs*?

18 What sort of creature is a drongo?

19 Manama is the capital of which country?

20 Which two nations are "The Low Countries"?

21 What is Crocodile Dundee's first name?

22 How many legs do arachnids have?

23 Who was British home secretary from 1979 to 1983?

24 What country was ruled by King Zog I until 1939?

25 Bamako is the capital of which African country?

26 Where is the International Court of Justice based?

27 Farouk I was king of which country until 1952?

28 *Finlandia* was written by which Finnish composer?

29 Who replaced Paul Keating as PM of Australia?

30 At least how many sides must a polygon have?

IT'S SAFER DOWN UNDER.

Answers on page 216

Knowall's question:

What mysterious phenomenon does a cereologist study?

BREAKFAST CEREALS !!!

1 In which Asian mountain range is the mysterious "abominable snowman" or yeti supposed to roam?

2 Prof. Steven Kaplan set up a research centre and hotline in New York to help what creatures of the night?

3 What did Colonel Robert Wilson famously but falsely claim to have photographed in 1934?

4 Why is the name of Kenneth Arnold revered by students of Unidentified Flying Objects?

5 The mythical "Kraken" feared by early mariners is now thought by to have been what sea creature?

6 What was seen in the sky over the American capital during the "Washington Invasion" in 1952?

7 Which children's author was certain that a photograph of girls playing with fairies in a garden was genuine?

8 What did the "dragons" sighted by visitors to the island of Komodo eventually prove to be?

9 Who established Project Sign (later Project Blue Book) and for what purpose?

10 John Ridgeway was doing what when he saw a massive 35-foot long sea serpent in 1966?

11 Which is "Britain's most haunted village", with ghosts that include a monk, red lady and screaming man?

12 What is the alternative name for the legendary North American wildman known as "Sasquatch" by Indians?

13 What great disaster did former seaman Morgan Robertson precisely predict in the novel *Futility*?

14 What did pilot Thomas Mantell claim to be doing in his P-51 Mustang when he lost radio contact and crashed?

15 Which famous crime novelist mysteriously disappeared for 11 days in December 1926?

16 What is the literal English translation of the German word "poltergeist"?

17 The American Department of Commerce has issued an official list of houses which share what peculiarity?

18 For what did the British psychic researcher Harry Price who died in 1948 become famous?

19 By what method did Patience Worth allegedly dictate novels to Emily Grant Hutchings and Pearl Curren?

20 Which organisation devoted to mystery lifted its ban on female members in September 1991?

21 What prophetic alphabet on 21 stones dating back to 2,000BC is still used to make predictions?

22 Which Israeli entertainer is famous for using "psychic powers" to bend cutlery and restart clocks?

23 Which area in the western Atlantic has claimed a large number of assorted craft in suspicious circumstances?

24 What exactly are NASA scientists searching for at the SETI institutes in North America?

25 In the West Indies, what is the name for the practice that includes sorcery, sacrifice and serpent worship?

26 Which ancient technique still used today involves the use of a forked stick to locate underground water?

27 "Dragon paths" are the Chinese name for which mystical lines of force on the Earth's surface?

28 Where do spiritualists believe that their contacts in the spirit world actually exist?

29 What name was given to the "small glowing man" seen by Kentucky farmers in 1955?

30 Various women have claimed to be which of Czar Nicholas II's daughters now known to have died in 1918?

HE'S GOING AROUND IN CIRCLES AGAIN.

Answers on page 216

QUIZ NUMBER 48

Knowall's question:

Which world number one tennis player was stabbed on court in 1993?

STEFFI GRAF !!!

1 In Italy, what is the Neapolitan equivalent of Sicily's feared Mafia?

2 Which lethal twin killed Jack "The Hat" McVitie in a dingy flat in London's East End?

3 In 1985, PC Keith Blakelock was savagely murdered on what North London estate?

4 Name the notorious Chicago hood who died of syphilis in Florida in 1947.

5 Which "great train robber" escaped British justice by settling in Brazil?

6 Name the civil servant acquitted of leaking Falklands War secrets to a Labour MP.

7 Whose high-security warehouse at Heathrow wasn't secure enough to protect £26 million in gold bullion?

8 Name the infamous pair of child killers nicknamed "The Moors Murderers".

9 In March 1981, disc jockey John Hinkley III shot and wounded which American president?

10 Which British diplomat was executed for treason in 1916 after trying to smuggle German arms to the IRA?

11 Name the Gloucester couple who were sensationally exposed as mass murderers in 1995.

12 Which member of the royal family survived a failed kidnap attempt by a gunman in 1974?

13 In which African country was British woman Julie Ward murdered in a game park?

14 He was acquitted of double murder on TV, then sued in the civil courts for the same crime in 1996. Who is he?

15 Name one of the three prisons which are located on the Isle of Wight.

16 Gunman Oliver Huberty slaughtered 20 people and wounded 16 at what California restaurant in 1984?

17 Name the nurse convicted in 1993 of killing four children at a Grantham hospital.

18 Clifford Irving was imprisoned for concocting a fake biography of which wealthy American recluse?

19 Which Italian known as "God's banker" was found hanging from London's Blackfriars Bridge in 1982?

20 Who did police arrest at a Hornsey bedsitter in 1983 in connection with 16 murders?

21 Name the two convicted murderers, one guilty and one innocent, who lived at 10 Rillington Place in London.

22 Hanged for shooting her lover David Blakely, who was the last women to be executed in Britain?

23 Which insurance fraudster was released in 1996 after serving time for a faked New York jewel robbery?

24 In 1967, Albert De Salvo was sentenced to prison for life in Massachusetts. How is he better known?

25 Who was hanged in 1962 for the "A6 murder" of Michael Gregsten at Deadman's Hill?

26 Which drug-crazed hippy clan murdered Hollywood actress Sharon Tate and others in 1969?

27 Who was hanged in 1953 for the murder of a policeman actually carried out by an under-age companion?

28 Which 19-year-old American heiress was abducted by the Simbionese Liberation Army in 1974?

29 Medical man. Fled with his lover. Captured by radio message. Hanged in 1910. Who was he?

30 Name the Swedish prime minister murdered on a Stockholm street in 1986.

Answers on page 216

Knowall's question:

Which actor specialising in gangster parts was a criminal in his youth and friend of notorious mobster "Bugsy" Siegel?

MICKEY ROONEY !!!

1 Name the area on the Burma-Laos-Thailand border which supplies much of the world's heroin.

2 Peter Sutcliffe confessed to 13 murders in 1987. What was his gruesome nickname?

3 1920s London housebreaker "Gussie" Delaney's daring rooftop raids introduced what phrase into English?

4 The crime fighters most feared by 1920s American gangsters were "T-men". What does the "T" stand for?

5 In 1992, which anti-Mafia judge was killed by a huge car bomb in Sicily?

6 Two 10-year-olds from Liverpool were charged with murdering which toddler in 1993?

7 In 1977, a Utah firing squad shot the first convict executed in America for 10 years. Who was he?

8 Name one of the two arch-villains who claimed the title "King of London's Underworld" in the 1930s and 1940s.

9 What were the last names of the 1930s American crime partnership of Bonnie and Clyde?

10 Which Mafia "don" is said to have been the role model for Marlon Brando's performance in *The Godfather*?

11 In 1968, which 11-year-old girl was sentenced to life detention for the manslaughter of two little boys?

12 Rodney Whitchelo was the first serious exponent of what new crime that started appearing in the 1980s?

13 In a massive bribery and gambling scandal, which baseball team "threw" America's 1919 World Series?

14 Who was the racketeering 1950s London landlord who was never convicted and died a millionaire?

15 In 1996, a fierce campaign to ban which weapons was started by bereaved parents from Dunblane?

16 In 1987, where in London did the safety deposit robbery thought to have netted £40 million take place?

17 In 1996, which convicted smuggler of Brinks-Mat gold vanished after a "road rage" killing in Kent?

18 What was the name of the gunman who tragically murdered 14 people at Hungerford in 1987?

19 In 1972, Agha Hasan Abedi founded what "caring bank that would nurture developing countries"?

20 What innocent part did Jack Mills and David Whitby play in the annals of British crime?

21 France's "public enemy number 1" and renowned escaper was killed by police in 1979. Who was he?

22 Which gangster was said to have yelled "don't shoot, G-men", coining the nickname for government agents?

23 Name one of the cities which are the main centres of Colombia's lucrative cocaine industry.

24 Name the South London family gang which was at daggers drawn with the Kray "firm" in the 1960s.

25 In what year was J. Edgar Hoover appointed chief of the FBI: 1924, 1928, 1932, 1936, 1940?

26 Which "killers for hire" group run by Albert Anastasia and Lepke Buchalter flourished in 1930s New York?

27 Name the car maker who cost British taxpayers millions and was acquitted on American drugs charges in 1984.

28 What was the nickname of the elite American anti-crime team led by Elliot Ness?

29 Which "lucky" mobster transformed the US Mafia from feuding hoods into an organised crime corporation?

30 In 1987, which soon-to-be-disgraced and convicted American bond dealer earned $550 million in salary?

YOU HAVE TO FLOAT ABOVE IT.

Answers on page 216

Knowall's question:

What is the name of President's Clinton's daughter?

PATTY !!!

1 Who had a No.1 hit album with *Born in the USA* in 1984?

2 Who was the original leader of the Black Panthers?

3 What is Madonna's surname?

4 What was John Wayne's last film, made in 1976?

5 What was Dwight D. Eisenhower's middle name?

6 What illness put Franklin Roosevelt in a wheelchair?

7 Who made his debut in *Steamboat Willie* (1928)?

8 Convict Robert Stroud was better known by what title?

9 Who is Mary Martin's famous soap opera son?

10 Who was the US Chief of Staff during the Gulf War?

11 In what 1953 film did Frank Sinatra win an Oscar?

12 What's the beagle dog's name in the Peanuts strip?

13 Who is uncle to Dewey, Huey and Louie?

14 What relationship to Elvis was Jesse Presley?

15 Which firm made Bill Gates a multi-billionnaire?

16 What actors teamed up in *The Fortune Cookie* (1966), *The Odd Couple* (1968) and *The Front Page* (1974)?

17 Which Republican presidential candidate was declared the winner of the 1948 election by the press – but lost?

18 Whose videoed beating by policemen, and their later acquittal by a white jury, led to Los Angeles riots?

19 In 1974, which Democrat defeated incumbent Gerald Ford to become the 39th President of the USA?

20 Unemployed Philadelphia heating engineer Charles Darrow invented which board game?

21 Whose best-selling book, originally entitled *Catch-17*, gave the English language the expression "Catch-22"?

22 Which Hollywood actor-director, following the path of an early movie, lives near Sundance, Utah?

23 After three years of neutrality, which US president decided "to make the world safe for democracy"?

24 In 1957, which playwright won the Pulitzer Prize for *Long Day's Journey Into Night*?

25 Which film director became an instant Hollywood success with *M*A*S*H** in 1971?

26 Who was the first American musical director of the New York Philharmonic Orchestra?

27 What was significant about the appointment of S. Day O'Connor as the 102nd Supreme Court Justice?

28 Which endearing duo won eight Oscars, including *Quiet Please* (1940) and *The Little Orphan* (1948)?

29 Which velvet-voiced black crooner had the original name Nathaniel Adams?

30 Catholic Elizabeth Bayley Seyton became the first American-born person to achieve what distinction?

THINK DAVID MELLOR.

Answers on page 217

Knowall's question:

Which enigmatic actor and playwright was knighted in 1970?

IT MUST BE LARRY !!!

1 What's the UK's longest-running television programme?

2 Where was the first safari park, opened in 1957?

3 Name two of the four members of *Beyond the Fringe*.

4 Who wrote the book *The Old Man of Lochnagar*?

5 Where were the *Queen Mary* and the *QE2* built?

6 Who created northern anti-hero Andy Capp?

7 In which sport did Eddie the Eagle represent Britain?

8 What is Britain's best-selling car of all time?

9 Who was director of the Royal Ballet from 1963 to 1970?

10 Whose signature tune was *Underneath the Arches*?

11 Which prime minister awarded The Beatles MBEs?

12 Who composed *Land of Hope and Glory* in 1902?

13 *Dear Me* was which writer-actor's autobiography?

14 What was the world's first jet fighter?

15 Which British pop star was knighted in 1995?

16 Name the suffragette who died after throwing herself under King George V's horse in the 1913 Derby.

17 What was Laker Airways' pioneering cheap service across the Atlantic introduced in 1977?

18 The composer Frederick Delius was born in which Yorkshire city?

19 Who designed the "bouncing bombs" used to break dams in Germany during World War 2?

20 Which comedy actor married Ann Howe, Britt Ekland, Miranda Quarry and Lynne Frederick?

21 What is the more common name for the Local Defence Volunteers, formed in 1940?

22 Which play by Howard Brenton led to the director's prosecution for obscenity in 1980?

23 Prime Minister Anthony Eden gave his name to what dress item he popularised in the 1930s and 1940s?

24 *The Lady's Not For Turning* was a verse play written by which dramatist in 1949?

25 With which equally mystical car did Rolls-Royce replace the Silver Ghost in 1926?

26 Dame Sybil Thorndike was the first British actress to appear where in 1982?

27 In 1962, who became a hit on *Thank Your Lucky Stars* with her catchphrase "Oi'll give it foive"?

28 Who was the first director-general of the BBC, responsible for shaping the organisation?

29 Which founder of ex-servicemen's homes was an observer on the second atomic attack on Japan?

30 Who was the fictional female detective created by Peter O'Donnell and immortalised in strip form?

DON'T BE FRIGHTENED TO SPEAK YOUR MIND.

Answers on page 217

Knowall's question:

Who is the patron saint of England?

SAINT JOHN !!!

1 Cedric Brown was dubbed "the most hated man in Britain" after his 1995 pay rise. With which company?

2 Better known for *Peter Pan*, who wrote *The Admirable Crichton* in 1902?

3 The original name of which business tycoon, once head of Lonrho, was Roland Fuhrhop?

4 What Cabinet post did Winston Churchill hold during World War 1?

5 Which Oscar-winning actress was elected Labour MP for Hampstead in 1992?

6 Which Labour politician from Wales is credited with creating the National Health Service?

7 Who was the last Liberal prime minister of Britain, heading a coalition government until 1922?

8 Name one of the parents-in-law of the present Queen Elizabeth.

9 Who was said to be "dumbfounded" when he was appointed Poet Laureate in 1972?

10 Nottingham University was founded with the assistance of which philanthropic chemist?

11 Which renowned England cricketer and footballer was offered the throne of Albania, but declined?

12 In 1953 the *Britannia* replaced which 50-year-old ship as the royal yacht?

13 Who wrote the stage play *A Man For All Seasons* and also wrote the screenplay?

14 What title did General Bernard Montgomery take when he became a viscount?

15 Which two London borough authorities did Margaret Thatcher consider her "flagship councils"?

16 Which Air Chief Marshal was in charge of RAF Fighter Command during the Battle of Britain?

17 Give one of the two first names of novelist and literary critic E. M. Forster.

18 In which year did Labour first gain an overall majority of seats in the House of Commons?

19 Who was the unlikely non-playing hero of the first FA Cup final held at Wembley in 1923?

20 Which influential film director made the first significant British "talkie", *Blackmail*, in 1929?

21 What was the significance of Margaret Bondfield's appointment as a minister in the 1929 government?

22 Which British actor described as "the second Olivier" was a roistering Tom Jones on screen?

23 Who was Prime Minister during the General Strike of 1926 and the Abdication Crisis ten years later?

24 Thought by many to be Britain's finest ever racing driver, he was killed at Hockenheim in 1968. Who was he?

25 Which German-born photographer who died in 1983 is regarded as a supreme observer of British life?

26 *The Planets* is the best-known work by which British composer, born in Cheltenham?

27 Which son of a tycoon became the world's biggest debtor in 1992 with debts of over £400 million?

28 Which great British landscape gardener who died in 1932 worked closely with Lutyens?

29 Which great British conductor trained the newly formed BBC Symphony Orchestra in 1931?

30 What title did car manufacturer Herbert Austin take when he became a peer?

ANOTHER DRAGON BITES THE DUST

Answers on page 217

Knowall's question:

What migratory animal does the snowy owl hunt?

THE CARIBOU ???

1 What type of plants are best equipped to survive the extemes of polar cold?

2 Who was the first man to make a complete polar trans-Antarctic crossing?

3 Largely in the Arctic Ocean, covered by an ice-cap, province of Denmark, population 56,000. What is it?

4 What "first" did American pilot William Byrd achieve in November 1929?

5 There is only one active volcano in Antarctica. What is its name?

6 Who sculpted the statue of polar hero Captain Robert Falcon Scott, located in Waterloo Place, London?

7 Who is generally accepted as the first man to reach the North Pole, though some still dispute his claim?

8 So-called fur seals are actually: bears, penguins, sea-lions, seals or whales?

9 The Beaufort Sea was named after Admiral Francis Beaufort (1774-1854). What else bears his name?

10 Antarctica is bigger than two other continents. Australasia/Oceania is one, but what is the other?

11 Name the Norwegian who used dog sleds to beat Captain Scott to the South Pole in 1911.

12 Antarctica contains what proportion of the world's fresh water: 50%, 60%, 70%, 80% or 90%?

13 What was the name of the Arctic ice station which provided the title of a 1963 novel by Alistair Maclean?

14 Name the British ship that was trapped and crushed by ice in the Weddell Sea in 1915.

15 In the fur trade, what name is given to the summer coat of the Arctic fox?

16 At 5,140m (16,863ft), Antarctica's tallest mountain is higher than Mont Blanc. What is it called?

17 For what was Captain "Titus" Oates initially responsible on Captain Scott's last expedition?

18 Name three of the five members of Scott's party that reached the South Pole in January 1912.

19 If the Antarctic's ice totally melted, by how much would the world's sea level rise: 25, 35, 45, 55 or 65 metres?

20 Which New Yorker was disgraced in 1909 when his false claim to be first to the North Pole was exposed?

21 What is the name of Britain's vast colonial territory in Antarctica, which includes the Graham Peninsula?

22 In 1926, which Italian flew over the North Pole in the airship *Norge*, dropping a cross at the magnetic pole?

23 Murdo Sound is the name of one of which country's permanent bases in the Antarctic?

24 Who was the first man to circumnavigate the Earth through both Poles?

25 What was unusual about Sir George Wilkins' trans-Arctic expedition in 1931?

26 What is the name of the largest island within Canada's Arctic region?

27 To the nearest 10 miles (16km) how much shorter is the Earth round the poles than round the equator?

28 Who made an epic voyage from Elephant Island to South Georgia in an open boat in 1916?

29 What is the correct term respectively for the male and female walrus?

30 In 1959, how many countries signed a treaty designed to protect Antarctica from exploitation: 6, 9, 12, 15, 20?

IT'S ENOUGH TO MAKE YOU SUICIDAL.

Answers on page 217

Knowall's question:

Which oil tanker ran aground in the Shetlands in 1993?

THE TORREY CANYON !!!

1 The pressure group Greenpeace was formed in which year: 1956, 1961, 1966, 1971, 1976?

2 What colour flag is flown on beaches that have been declared clean and free of avoidable pollution?

3 A leak from an American-owned chemical factory in what Indian city killed tens of thousands in 1984?

4 Britain's nuclear treatment centre is Thorp, at Sellafield in Cumbria. What do the letters stand for?

5 In 1962, American Rachel Carson published *Silent Spring*, warning against the ecological dangers of what?

6 In which country is Chernobyl, scene of the world's worst nuclear accident in 1986?

7 What are the chemicals in aerosols and refrigerants partly responsible for the depletion of the ozone layer?

8 What is the destructive cultivation technique used by nomadic peoples in many Third World countries?

9 In a 1993 survey, which European city was declared the least polluted: Athens, London, Madrid, Paris, Rome?

10 Name one of the countries that has consistently flouted agreements on whaling or refused to sign them.

11 Among Europe's main rivers, which one has been officially classified as the most polluted?

12 In 1992, where was the first Earth Summit (of the World Commission on Environment and Development) held?

13 What was the Worldwide Fund for Nature called until it changed its name in 1988?

14 What mammal is particularly affected by chemical pollution in the estuaries of eastern North America?

15 One of Britain's most powerful environmental pressure groups is the CPRE. What do the letters stand for?

16 The deforestation of hillsides in Nepal has led to the silting up of river deltas in which Asian country?

17 A 50-year ban on mining was signed by all relevant countries in 1991 concerning which part of the world?

18 The UK's first commercial wind farm began to generate elctricity in 1992. In what English county?

19 The "crown of thorns" starfish is responsible for the depletion of coral at which World Heritage Site?

20 What was the nationality of the two scientists who first identified a "hole" in the ozone layer over Antarctica?

21 Who is the American lawyer who led many successful consumer campaigns in the 1960s and 1970s?

22 What water bird is the symbol of the Royal Society for the Protection of Birds?

23 The proportion of which harmful gas in the atmosphere is increased with the destruction of the rainforests?

24 What is the vast belt of semi-arid land and savannah south of the Sahara suffering from "desertification"?

25 Name the Greenpeace vessel blown up in Auckland harbour by the French secret service in 1985.

26 What is the principal pollutant gas present in acid rain, formed by the burning of fossil fuels?

27 Which EEC member country has the highest percentage of both recycled paper and glass?

28 What killed over 4,000 people in London and other cities and led to the Clean Air Act of 1956?

29 In 1979, where in Pennsylvania did the United States' worst nuclear accident occur?

30 Which gas, created by processing waste material, can be harnessed to produce electric power?

HE SHOULD GET ON THE BUNNY.

Answers on page 218

Knowall's question:

The science of map and chart making is known as what?

SURVEYING !!!

1 Which sign of the zodiac is represented by a ram?

2 What are the official languages of the Vatican City?

3 Amethyst is a form of which mineral?

4 What is the name given to the eve of All Saints Day?

5 Name an American state that contains the letter "x".

6 Where was Florence Nightingale born?

7 What is the unit of sound measurement?

8 In a culinary context, what is rocket?

9 Who is the lead singer of Pulp?

10 What was the nationality of writer Franz Kafka?

11 Which metal is represented by the symbol *Na*?

12 How many sides does a icosahedron have?

13 What is the term for someone who makes arrows?

14 Which motorway links Manchester and Leeds?

15 Which recent American president was called "Poppy"?

16 What was abolished In 1988 when it cost 37 pence?

17 What country gives the Order of the Chrysanthemum?

18 What is an alternative name for the knight in chess?

19 Who wrote the plays *Jumpers* and *Arcadia*?

20 Where in France is an annual 24-hour motor race held?

21 Whose motto is *Honi soit qui mal y pense*?

22 Which annual arts festival was inaugurated in 1947?

23 In heraldry, what is meant by "rampant"?

24 What is the currency of the British Virgin Islands?

25 Which day precedes Ash Wednesday?

26 What is the highest rank in the US Army?

27 To which country do the Faroe Islands belong?

28 Who lit the Olympic flame at the 1996 Atlanta games?

29 What make of car were Imps and Huskies?

30 Who did Tony Blair replace as Labour Party leader?

CART BEFORE THE HORSE.

Answers on page 218

Knowall's question:

Which powerful Australian won the 1971 Wimbledon women's singles title?

MARGARET COURT !!!

1 What Norweigian seaport is the largest town north of the Arctic Circle?

2 Name the Trotskyist faction expelled from the Labour Party in 1986.

3 Which Middle East ruler was driven into exile by Muslim fundamentalists in 1979?

4 What girl's name was invented by J. M. Barrie in *Peter Pan* and is still used to this day?

5 Which is the odd one out: baseball, cricket, tennis or table tennis?

6 What is the name of marks resembling Christ's wounds which appear on a living body?

7 Which British cartoonist is best remembered for his portrayal of the awful schoolgirls of St Trinian's?

8 At what London theatre was an opera and ballet company founded by Lilian Baylis in 1931?

9 Which American senator chaired the Northern Ireland peace talks in 1996?

10 In 1996, what car company clinched a £72 million aid package to ensure its new model would be British?

11 With which group did Cliff Richard make a number of hit records in the 1960s?

12 What town in West Yorkshire is situated where the Rivers Holme and Colne meet?

13 Which former TV lottery queen said: "I'm sure there will be a time when I pencil motherhood in."?

14 Hundreds were injured and 66 died when barriers collapsed at which Scottish football ground in 1971?

15 Which two eastern American states are divided by the Mason-Dixon line?

16 In the Vietnam War, what was the jungle supply line from north to south called?

17 Which colour is the odd one out: black, cyan, green, magenta, yellow?

18 What nationality was Madame Marie Tussaud, founder of the London waxworks which burned down in 1925?

19 In 1956, who took the one Australian wicket that didn't fall to Jim Laker in the Test match at Old Trafford?

20 Which is the odd one out: The A-Team, Power Rangers, The Incredible Hulk, Superman?

21 Which Italian motorcyclist won a record 15 world championship titles between 1966 and 1975?

22 What was the nationality of UN Secretary General Pérez de Cuéllar?

23 By what name are the Tower of London's ceremonial yeoman warders known?

24 Which pilot who lost both legs in a pre-war flying accident served in the RAF during World War 2?

25 What is the London venue for the annual Promenade Concerts held in conjunction with the BBC?

26 Name the British athlete who announced in 1996: "I think I am the biggest morale-booster to the team."

27 *The Outsider*, *The Plague* and *The Rebel* were written by which French existentialist?

28 An IRA bomb at the Houses of Parliament killed which Conservative MP and former Colditz POW in 1979?

29 Which international opera festival takes place near Lewes in East Sussex each year?

30 What nation has the unique distinction of competing in every summer and winter Olympics since 1896?

HE'S HOPING FOR A MEDAL.

Answers on page 218

Knowall's question:

What did the USA buy from Denmark for $25 million in 1917?

BACON !!!

1 What is the only animal to sleep regularly on its back?

2 Until 1960, what coin was a quarter of a penny?

3 In World War 2, what did "careless talk" cost?

4 Which Chicago building has 16,000 windows?

5 In which city is Cornwall's only cathedral?

6 What do the letters HB stand for on a pencil?

7 Name the currency unit of Brazil.

8 What is bladder wrack?

9 Who began in showbiz as Boy Bruce the Mighty Atom?

10 Which Channel Island has an area of 9 square miles?

11 Which planet is closest to the Sun?

12 Globe and Jerusalem are types of what vegetable?

13 Who became the Governor of Hong Kong in 1992?

14 The Faroes lie between the Shetlands and where?

15 What is President Jimmy Carter's middle name?

16 For what sport is Cowdray Park famous?

17 Who donates the Trafalgar Square Christmas tree?

18 How many *Carry On* films were made: 12, 17, 23, 28, 34?

19 What is the American slang word for 10 cents?

20 Sussex, field and clumber are all what?

21 Name the two countries bordering Tunisia.

22 What is half a sphere called?

23 In what month is London's Lord Mayor's Show?

24 What are Trinity, Michaelmas and Hilary?

25 How many bones in a human skull: 1, 4, 9, 14, 22?

26 Which metal is refined from bauxite?

27 What do otter hounds hunt?

28 Which country has the most international borders?

29 How old did women have to be to vote in 1918?

30 In which British city is The Royal Mile?

HE'S BLESSED WITH A VIVID IMAGINATION.

Answers on page 219

Knowall's question:

Which American dramatist wrote *Cat on a Hot Tin Roof*?

ARTHUR MILLER !!!

1 Which novel by Laurie Lee is a nostalgic account of a childhood in the Cotswolds?

2 What is the title of George Orwell's anti-Soviet farmyard fable?

3 Which Pulitzer prize-winning book by black writer Alice Walker was made into a Steven Spielberg film?

4 What subject does Sophie learn in Jostein Gaarder's novel *Sophie's World*?

5 What is the title of the first book in Lawrence Durrell's *Alexandria Quartet*?

6 On which painter's life is the novel *The Moon and Sixpence* by W. Somerset Maugham based?

7 Which two famous poets appear in Pat Barker's *Regeneration* trilogy, set in the First World War?

8 What is the name of the house featured in Daphne du Maurier's *Rebecca*?

9 Who was the character Dill in Harper Lee's novel *To Kill A Mockingbird* based on?

10 Which novelist famous for her 'Aga sagas' wrote *The Choir* and *The Rector's Wife*?

11 Which best-selling British thriller writer announced his retirement in 1996?

12 Which continent does Wilbur Smith use as the setting for most of his books?

13 Which playwright and screenwriter wrote *The Birthday Party* and *The Caretaker*?

14 Which amusing, diary-keeping schoolboy character was created by Sue Townsend?

15 Which gay writer wrote *The Swimming-Pool Library* and *The Folding Star*?

16 Which irrepressible family features in H.E. Bates' *The Darling Buds of May*?

17 What is the full name of Richmal Crompton's naughty schoolboy hero?

18 Which writer was the founder-editor of *Gramophone* magazine and wrote the comic novel *Whisky Galore*?

19 Which fictional town in the USA does Garrison Keillor write about?

20 Who was the tragic novelist sister of the Bloomsbury painter Vanessa Bell?

21 What is the name of the book on which the film *Schindler's List* is based, and who wrote it?

22 Which father and son authors respectively wrote *The Old Devils* and *The Rachel Papers*?

23 Which town completes the John Betjeman quote: "Come, friendly bombs, and fall on ......!"?

24 What breed of dog did Dodie Smith feature in the book that was later made into a Walt Disney film?

25 Who wrote the explicitly autobiographical television play *The Singing Detective* and *Pennies From Heaven*?

26 What is the name of the "gentleman's gentleman" who features in P. G. Wodehouse's books?

27 What is the profession of Muriel Spark's feisty Scot Miss Jean Brodie?

28 Which was the first of Beatrix Potter's children's books to be published?

29 Which best-selling woman novelist sailed around the world single-handed?

30 What is the name of John Buchan's hero who first appeared in *The Thirty-Nine Steps*?

NASHVILLE HERE WE COME.

Answers on page 219

Knowall's question:

Which female novelist penned the advertising slogan "go to work on an egg"?

EDWINA CURRIE !!!

1 Which author of children's books wrote *The Railway Children* and novels about the young Bastables?

2 Which Toni Morrison novel that won the 1993 Nobel Prize for Literature deals with slavery and infanticide?

3 Which war is the setting for Ernest Hemingway's *For Whom the Bell Tolls*?

4 Which novel by Nicholas Evans is about a man who soothes a traumatised horse and its owner?

5 Which famous children's author went to Russia in 1913 and married Trotsky's former secretary in 1924?

6 Which publicity-shy American novelist wrote *The Catcher in the Rye*?

7 Which novel by American writer Jack London tells the story of a sledge-dog in the Yukon?

8 Which city is the setting for the Christopher Isherwood novels that feature Sally Bowles?

9 Which prolific playwright was a strict vegetarian, never drank spirits, tea, or coffee, and lived to be 94?

10 Which book by Jack Kerouac describing a marathon car journey achieved cult status in the 1950s?

11 What area of England is used as the setting for Graham Swift's novel *Waterland*?

12 Who wrote the novels *The History of the World in 10½ Chapters* and *Flaubert's Parrot*?

13 Which Dublin-born poet and playwright, interested in the paranormal, wrote *The Wild Swans at Coole*?

14 Which Canadian novelist explored the theatre and academia in *The Cornish Trilogy*?

15 Which novelist was married to naturalist Peter Scott and writer Kingsley Amis?

16 Which chaotic family lived at Stella Gibbons' *Cold Comfort Farm*?

17 Which eccentric short-story writer cabled to his wife: "Am in Market Harborough. Where ought I to be?"?

18 Which book by Carol Shields traces the life of Daisy Goodwill from birth to death?

19 Which Australian author wrote *The Thorn Birds* and *The Ladies of Missalonghi*?

20 Which character is the narrator in Evelyn Waugh's *Brideshead Revisited*?

21 In which Joe Orton play do a couple of bank robbers hide their stolen money in a coffin?

22 For which animal fable is West Country writer Henry Williamson most famous?

23 Which German author's daughter did W. H. Auden marry to provide her with a British passport?

24 What is the name of the heroine in Thomas Hardy's *Far from the Madding Crowd*?

25 Which city is the centre of political corruption and racial tension in Tom Wolfe's *The Bonfire of the Vanities*?

26 Which female post-war novelist was a fellow and tutor in philosophy at Oxford?

27 Which Poet Laureate wrote the children's novel *The Box of Delights*?

28 Which novel by Hanif Kureishi won the Whitbread Award and was later turned into a television drama?

29 Which Irish author of *The Riddle of the Sands* was tried and executed for treason?

30 Which writer of historical biographies is married to playwright Harold Pinter?

GET OUT THE BLOW TORCH.

Answers on page 219

Knowall's question:

Which respected writer was a World War 1 ambulance driver and secret agent?

ERNEST HEMINGWAY !!!

1 The autobiography of which *Beyond the Fringe* member, principally a playwright, is entitled *Writing Home*?

2 Which book by Kazuo Ishiguro describes an elderly butler's recollection of domestic service in the 1930s?

3 What is the title of the 1,349-page novel about post-independence India by Vikram Seth?

4 Whose poems were inspired by an idealised view of rural Shropshire?

5 Who was the poetess wife of Ted Hughes who committed suicide?

6 Which character in *Sons and Lovers* is based on D. H. Lawrence's own mother?

7 Which book studies the relationships of a group of schoolboys marooned on a desert island?

8 What is the title of Vladimir Nabokov's novel that describes a man's obsession with a pubescent girl?

9 What are the first names of the Schegel sisters in E. M. Forster's *Howards End*?

10 In which play did Madame Arcati and Elvira feature, and who wrote it?

11 Which American hell-raiser won his second Pulitzer Prize with *The Executioner's Song*?

12 Which Dorset town is the setting of John Fowles' *The French Lieutenant's Woman*?

13 How old was Daisy Ashford when she wrote *The Young Visiters*?

14 Which Irish author wrote *The Country Girls Trilogy*, banned by the Irish Censorship Board?

15 Paul Scott's *Raj Quartet* was adapted to become which highly acclaimed television series?

16 Who wrote the story of Rat, Mole, Badger, and Toad and what is it called?

17 From which book did Philip Roth earn about a million dollars from extracts before it was published?

18 Which American author wrote *The Accidental Tourist*, later made into a successful film?

19 On which island did the writer Robert Graves live for most of his adult life?

20 Which novel by John Steinbeck tells the story of the Joad family, who work as fruit-pickers in California?

21 Which poet introduced quirky typographical techniques in his work, including using no capital letters?

22 In which Truman Capote novel does the dizzy female character Holly Golightly appear?

23 Which playwright wanted to be an actor and started writing to provide himself with leading roles?

24 Which of F. Scott Fitzgerald's novels was inspired by his wife's breakdowns and his alcoholism?

25 What book by which Irish writer was first published in Paris in 1922 but banned in Britain until 1937?

26 Which Mary Wesley novel is based on five cousins and their relationships during World War 2?

27 The original typesetter refused to finish the sexually explicit novel *Fear of Flying*. Who wrote it?

28 Name one of the three well-known Liverpool poets whose work in the 1960s was written to be read in public.

29 Which book by William Styron tells the story of a Polish woman who survived Auschwitz?

30 Which aristocratic writer, married to Harold Nicolson, inspired Virginia Woolf's *Orlando*?

TAUNTON HERE WE COME.

Answers on page 219

Knowall's question:

Who played *Dr Who* on his return to television in 1996?

ROGER DALTREY !!!

1 Who coined the phrase "science fiction", and is seen by many as the genre's modern founding father?

2 In which science fiction writer's work can the Ankh-Morpork Watch and golems be found?

3 Which 25th-century champion does battle with the Mongols and Killer Kane?

4 What, destined to become a staple ingredient of sci-fi, did Karel Capek introduce in his 1920 play *R.U.R.*?

5 What catastrophe forms the backdrop to Nevil Shute's dystopian novel *On the Beach*?

6 In which science fiction classic by John Wyndham are humans stalked by deadly mobile plants?

7 Which gigantic reptilian monster was the first and most famous of Inoshiro Honda's creations?

8 According to Douglas Adams, what number is "The answer to the Great Question of . . . Everything"?

9 Which eminent sci-fi novelist turned his attentions away from fantasy to write *The Empire of the Sun*?

10 Who helped to establish science fiction as a literary genre with works such as *Non-Stop* and *Greybeard*?

11 Which Anthony Burgess novel presents a bleak future vision of England terrorised by teenage hoodlums?

12 Who plays the *Running Man* in the film based on a story by Stephen King?

13 In George Orwell's *1984*, what is the name of the omniscient overseer who may or may not exist?

14 What is the title of Arthur C. Clarke's sequel to *2001: A Space Odyssey*?

15 Who adapted H.G. Wells' book *The War of the Worlds* into a 1930s radio serial that panicked America?

16 What is the name of Sigourney Weaver's character in the sequence of *Alien* films?

17 In which Aldous Huxley novel are humans hatched from incubators and reared in communal nurseries?

18 Norman Bean was a pseudonym for which early 20th-century writer of science fiction?

19 Who directed the comical but pessimistic film vision of the future, *Brazil*?

20 What shocking experience prompted Kurt Vonnegut to write his apocalyptic novel *Slaughterhouse 5*?

21 Who propounded the "Three Laws of Robotics" to which all droids should comply?

22 The rock 'n' roll musical *Return to the Forbidden Planet* was based on which Shakespearean play?

23 What does a young boy witness in Chris Marker's time-travelling tale, *La Jetée*?

24 Who wrote the story on which Ridley Scott's film *Bladerunner* is based?

25 Which writer created Jerry Cornelius, hero of *The English Assassin*?

26 How are the years 1939-43 affectionately known by lovers of the science fiction genre?

27 In which film is an android played by Arnold Schwarzenegger sent back from the future?

28 *The Demolished Man* and *Tiger! Tiger!* are novels by which influential science fiction writer?

29 Which sinister Orwellian chamber contains all of our greatest fears?

30 Who influenced murderous hippy guru Charles Manson with his novel *Stranger in a Strange Land*?

PERHAPS HE MEANT ROGER McDALTREY.

Answers on page 219

Knowall's question:

Which romatic novelist's books have been borrowed more than any other writer's from British libraries?

BARBARA CARTLAND'S !!!

1 Tory MP Rupert Allason writes espionage books using what pen name?

2 Which former Tory MP wrote *The Fourth Estate* and *First Among Equals*?

3 Who is the Tory MP who made her authorial debut with the political sizzler *A Parliamentary Affair*?

4 In which book is General Woundwort defeated by Hazel, Bigwig and Fiver?

5 What Frederick Forsyth novel features a former CIA agent fighting the return of Russian dictatorship?

6 Which author wrote *The Green Mile*, unusually published by Penguin in six spaced paperback parts?

7 What company sponsors a well-established series of guides to motoring and star-rated eateries in France?

8 *The Forsyte Saga* was written by which winner of a Nobel Prize for Literature?

9 Name the American writer who keenly observes the world in books like *Notes from a Small Island*?

10 Crime writer Barbara Vine is perhaps better known by what other name?

11 Name the popular British writer who first made his name with *The Virgin Soldiers*.

12 Which Hollywood wife had a massive hit with the pulsating *Hollywood Wives*?

13 Who extended bully Flashman's escapades beyond his original schooldays?

14 The works of which writer of steamy romances are half-jokingly described as "The Rutshire Novels"?

15 Who began his surge to authorial superstardom with the gripping tale of a defecting Soviet submarine?

16 A copy of each new book by which author who once worked for her is hand-delivered to the Queen Mother?

17 In the 1960s, the paperback of what Hobbit saga by J. R. R. Tolkien sold a million copies a year in the USA?

18 Which humorous author followed *Porterhouse Blue* with the long-awaited sequel *Grantchester Grind*?

19 What venerable reference work packed with world facts and figures published its 105th edition in 1966?

20 Who created *The Story of Painting*, a nun's-eye view of western art to accompany her television series?

21 In which comedian and writer's *Popcorn* did a Hollywood film director find death imitating art?

22 The chronicler of "Wessex" and its people died in 1928. Who was he?

23 In 1966, which American crime author was rocked by allegations of an affair with a married ex-FBI agent?

24 Which South African writer followed the adventures of the Courtney family over several generations?

25 Which English author wrote *Brighton Rock, Our Man in Havana* and *Travels with My Aunt*?

26 What is the name of the Crime Writers' annual award for the best crime novel?

27 In which university city does Colin Dexter's enigmatic Inspector Morse operate?

28 Which English-born writer is said to be America's highest-earning romantic novelist?

29 Published annually, what is the "bible" of cricket buffs throughout the world?

30 Which respected author with an actress sister writes under the name John le Carré?

NOW HE'S COOKING.

Answers on page 220

Knowall's question:

In 1905 a group of artists led by Henri Matisse were nicknamed "Les Fauvres". What does the name mean?

THE POOR ONES !!!

1 Which cult figure in the 1960s and exponent of American "pop art" depicted Campbell's soup cans?

2 Which Surrealist Spanish painter was notorious for his extravagant and eccentric statements about himself?

3 Which Cornish village known for an artists' colony in the 1940s has an outpost of the Tate Gallery?

4 Which Italian painter, who died tragically aged 35 in 1920, used sculptural effects in his portraits and nudes?

5 What innovative painting style pioneered by Picasso was banned from a Paris exhibition in 1913?

6 The reclining figure in bronze was the favourite theme of which abstract English sculptor?

7 Name the London gallery which is infamous for buying and exhibiting a pile of bricks.

8 In 1952, which Dutch-born American artist's series *Women* used violent imagery and caused a sensation?

9 Which Italian society painter who died in 1988 had notable success with his paintings of British royalty?

10 What nationality was Edvard Munch, whose painting *The Scream* was stolen and recovered in the 1990s?

11 The work of which Dutch painter includes rectangles of primary colours, divided by a flat grid of black lines?

12 Which Yorkshire-born artist who settled in California painted *A Bigger Splash* in 1967?

13 What is the name for the technique that combines materials such as paper, fabric or photos with painting?

14 Which Swiss sculptor and painter is famed for his delicate emaciated figures?

15 Who paints primarily portraits and nudes and is the grandson of the founder of psychoanalysis?

16 Which English painter designed the stained glass windows for the new Coventry cathedral?

17 Which Russian painter is generally considered to be the pioneer of abstract painting?

18 Which American-born British sculptor's symbolic statue *Adam* brought accusations of blasphemy in 1939?

19 Which Swiss painter, whose work is often threaded with fantasy and wit, painted *A Young Lady's Adventure*?

20 Which British textile magnate, art collector and patron donated his collection to the University of London?

21 Which legendary American painter, who died in a road accident, experimented with drip and action painting?

22 Which British sculptor, born in 1956, works largely in the open air and uses materials he finds around him?

23 By what name is the famous American primitive painter who took up painting in her old age known?

24 Which English painter set many of his religious paintings in Cookham, Berkshire, where he lived?

25 Which 23-year-old Russian-born artist renowned for his fanciful painting first arrived in Parls in 1910?

26 Which portrait of a physician painted by whom was sold for £44,378,696 in 1990?

27 Which two artist members of the Bloomsbury Group lived together at Charleston, Sussex?

28 In 1911, which famous portrait was stolen by an Italian from the Louvre in Paris?

29 The late works of which great French painter included collages of cut-out, painted paper shapes?

30 Which Mexican painter famous for murals of industrial life decorated the Californian Stock Exchange?

TRUST HIM TO BE BEASTLY.

Answers on page 220

Knowall's question:

Which city used £100,000 of Lottery money to help purchase a giant marble "pebble" by sculptor Kan Yasuda in 1996?

ABERDEEN !!!

1 Whose characteristic subject was industrial northern England, peopled by matchstick-like figures?

2 Which Spaniard who settled in Paris used cryptic signs and hallucinogenic forms inspired by extreme hunger?

3 Which American woman painted magnified botanical subjects and the arid landscape of New Mexico?

4 Name the Scottish shipping magnate who died in 1958, whose art collection formed a new Glasgow gallery.

5 Which Welsh-born artist who in his youth lived with gypsies had a sister who was also a painter?

6 Which painter specialising in old Montmartre was the illegitimate son of French artist Suzanne Valadon?

7 Which art and design movement in the early years of the century is characterised by writhing plant forms?

8 To which influential British sculptor was abstract artist Ben Nicholson once married?

9 In which landlocked European country was the Dada movement started in 1916?

10 Whose controversial portrait of Sir Winston Churchill was later destroyed by Churchill's wife?

11 Which prolific Spanish painter had a "blue period" and is probably the most famous artist of the 20th century?

12 Which much admired but reclusive French artist died at his Aix-en-Provence home in 1906?

13 Which American "pop art" painter, sculptor and master of the magnified comic strip painted *Whaam*?

14 Which Dublin-born painter creates gory figures and is considered Britain's most important post-war artist?

15 What term is given to artistic creations that involve some sort of physical movement?

16 Which American artist, sculptor and printmaker born in 1930 painted *Flag*, *Target* and *Maps*?

17 In 1904, which French Impressionist's 37 "Views of the Thames at London" were shown in Paris?

18 What 195m wide, 172m tall statue was started in 1948 and will not be finished until the next century?

19 Which member of the royal family paints watercolours, exhibits widely and has illustrated a book?

20 Name the notorious artist who exhibited a sheep preserved in formaldehyde in the 1990s.

21 What nationality was Gustav Klimt, who painted women in rich colours with a linear construction?

22 Rachel Whiteread won the 1993 Turner Prize for a concrete cast of what in London's East End?

23 Which Belgian Surrealist is best remembered for painting a man with an apple suspended in front of his face?

24 American painter and photographer Man Ray also specialised in what other art form?

25 In which striking modern building is the Paris Museum of Modern Art situated?

26 Which English artist did appealing child studies used to illustrate her children's stories and many postcards?

27 Which art historian and surveyor of the Queen's pictures was exposed as a Soviet spy?

28 The English cartoonist married to Jane Asher is known for violent caricatures of public figures. Who is he?

29 Which oil tycoon left a substantial fortune to endow the Malibu, California art gallery that bears his name?

30 Which celebrated French primitive painter known as "Le Douanier" ("the customs officer") died in 1910?

UNITED WE FALL.

Answers on page 220

Knowall's question:

Where is the world's tallest inhabitable building?

CHICAGO !!!

1. Name the French museum which is home to a giant glass pyramid designed by Ieoh Ming Pei.

2. Which British building, completed in 1951, became a major international influence on concert-hall design?

3. After which celebrated scientist did Erich Mendelshon name his tower in Potsdam?

4. How was the influential Swiss-born French architect Charles-Edouard Jeanneret better known?

5. Which Scottish architect's most famous work is the Glasgow School of Art, completed in 1907?

6. In 1996 which British architect proposed a Millennium tower for London, to be Europe's tallest building?

7. What type of building was of primary interest to the Chicago School of architects?

8. Which *avant garde* Australian landmark was designed by the Dane Jorn Utzon?

9. Name the artist renowned for enveloping buildings and structures in vast sheets of coloured fabric.

10. What significant movement was founded in 1919 by Walter Gropius at Weimar, Germany?

11. Which of the "new" universities built in the 1960s was designed by Sir Denys Lasdun?

12. What is the name of the 1988 extension to London's National Gallery?

13. Who was responsible for rebuilding the bomb-damaged House of Commons after World War 2?

14. From the top of which 533 metres (1,815ft) Toronto building can diners see hills 75 miles (121km) away?

15. Which famous Viennese architect is considered by many to be the founder of the "Modern Movement"?

16 What is the name of the major gallery in New York designed by Frank Lloyd Wright?

17 Which palatial glass London structure by Joseph Paxton was destroyed by fire on 30 November 1936?

18 Whose masterwork is the unfinished Expiatory Temple of the Sagrada Familia in Barcelona?

19 The Olivier Auditorium, Cottesloe Studio and Lyttleton Theatre can all be found where, precisely?

20 Architect Richard Rogers designed which major Paris landmark with Renzo Piano in the 1970s?

21 What is the name of the new Brazilian capital for which Lucio Costa drew up plans in 1957?

22 From which European country did the Constructivists (or "artist-engineers") emerge during World War 1?

23 In which English city did Sir Basil Spence reconstruct the cathedral destroyed during World War 2?

24 Who famously described the London's South Bank National Theatre as a "nuclear power station" in 1988?

25 Which architectural group designed buildings made up of primary colours and interlocking geometrical forms?

26 Britain's then-tallest building at 198 metres (650ft), opened in London in 1965. What was its original name?

27 Name the landmark London office building left empty by developer Harry Hyams in the 1960s.

28 Which famous art deco New York skyscraper opened in 1930, a year before the Empire State Building?

29 What dam on the Columbia River completed in 1942 contains Franklin D. Roosevelt Lake?

30 The elegant "tented" stand designed at Lord's cricket ground by Michael Hopkins is called what?

LIKE IT OR LUMP IT.

Answers on page 220

Knowall's question:

What is the claim to fame of Virility Alley in Ripatransone, Italy?

IT'S VERY LONG !!!

1. Who was the first woman tennis player ever to win a $1 million prize?

2. How many pounds in weight make a stone in imperial measurement?

3. In chess, what is the only move where a player can move two pieces at once?

4. What was the first sport ever to be broadcast on BBC Television?

5. Give one of the two middle names of former American President George Bush.

6. At the last count (1996), how many countries in the world were headed by a sovereign: 26, 36, 46, 56, 66?

7. In 1967, which two soccer clubs were involved in the first-ever all-London FA Cup final?

8. What's the greatest number of times a single sheet of paper can be successfully folded?

9. The feral population of which large rodent was thought to have been eliminated from East Anglia by the 1980s?

10. Which four countries does the region known as Kurdistan encompass?

11. What Beatles song has the line: "Father MacKenzie writing the words of a sermon no one will hear."?

12. Who successfully completed the first ascent of Mt Everest with Edmund Hillary in 1953?

13. Who became the militant president of the National Union of Mineworkers in 1981?

14. Who was Mamas and Papas singer Michelle Phillips married to for eight days?

15. Which metallic element is represented by the chemical symbol *Ag*?

16 Only two American presidents have ever declared their religion as "not affiliated". Name one of them.

17 What distinction is enjoyed by the village of Sutton-under-Whitestonecliffe in Yorkshire?

18 Who was the oldest driver to win the Formula 1 world motor-racing championship?

19 When India and Pakistan were divided in 1947, which northern state was – and remains – a disputed area?

20 Which standard piece of sports equipment is 107 centimetres (42in) long?

21 What great popular myth was exploded by American astronaut James Lovell?

22 Which American city is the undisputed capital of country 'n' western music?

23 Roughly how many times does the human heart beat in 10 years: 70, 170, 270, 370 or 470 million?

24 What animal must stand at least 17 hands tall to meet the breed standard?

25 Of which country did Brian Mulroney become the prime minister in 1984?

26 What is the correct term for a wristwatch that has hands and a dial?

27 The 1943 film *Lassie Come Home* featured which 11-year-old British-born actress who is still going strong?

28 How many Grand Slam tennis titles did the great Billie-Jean King win: 24, 29, 34, 39, 44?

29 Where do North Utsire and South Utsire appear without fail every day?

30 To the nearest thousand, what is the annual average number of murders in the USA during the 1990s?

THINK BREADTH RATHER THAN LENGTH.

Answers on page 221

Knowall's question:

Which character said wistfully:
"I am a Bear of very Little Brain
and long words Bother me."?

RUPERT BEAR !!!

1. Which 2,200 square mile (5,698sq km) area of Britain does not have a single traffic light?

2. What did British troops seize in a swift dawn raid on 19 October 1951?

3. Who won the 1996 presidential election in Russia despite health worries?

4. In boxing, what is the name of the class for fighters weighing 7st 10lb (49kg) or less?

5. In what year did the first TV go on sale in America for $75: 1924, 1928, 1932, 1936, 1940?

6. Who is the hellraising actor father of Cherie, wife of Labour's Tony Blair?

7. Who was the first British driver ever to win the Formula 1 world motor-racing championship?

8. The playing surface of which new stadium at Wembley was laid in 1922?

9. Which frogman vanished in Portsmouth harbour in 1957 while covertly inspecting Soviet warships?

10. In how many of the world's countries do cars drive on the left: 4, 13, 21, 33, 42?

11. In 1954, who became the youngest jockey ever to ride a Derby winner at the age of 18?

12. How many numbered "slots" does a conventional roulette wheel contain?

13. Zionists blew up a wing of which Jerusalem hotel used as the British Army HQ in 1946?

14. Which American president was related to 11 others, five by blood and six by marriage?

15. What is Britain's premier annual dog show, which has been held for over 100 years?

16 The most most popular street name in America is: 1st Street, 2nd Street, Elm Street, Independence Street?

17 Which British PM accepted a car and £30,000-worth of biscuit shares to run it for life in 1924?

18 Which 19-year-old actor did 23-year-old movie star Joan Crawford marry in 1929?

19 Which county is the only one to have won both cricket's knockout tournaments in one season?

20 What caring service to "benefit all the people of Great Britain" began on 5 July 1948?

21 In 1987, which Swede was the first postwar male to win a Wimbledon singles match without losing a game?

22 How many feet of electrical wiring does the average car have: 1,500, 2,000, 2,500, 3,000, 3,500?

23 Which Harrow schoolboy was named King of Jordan in August 1952?

24 What country has increased in size by 19% since medieval times as a result of reclamation from the sea?

25 In what popular pastime are boilies, buzzers and bivvies used?

26 What "first" did presenters Richard Dimbleby and Alan Adair achieve in Calais on 27 August 1950?

27 Anthony Andrews and Jon Finch were the original choice to play Bodie and Doyle in which TV series?

28 How many James Bond films did the late producer Cubby Broccoli make: 9, 11, 13, 15, 17?

29 What was the name of the world's then-largest liner, which was destroyed by fire in 1920?

30 Which batsman ended the 1947 cricket season with a record 3,816 first-class runs, including 18 centuries?

NICE TRY, BUT IT STINKS.

Answers on page 221

Knowall's question:

Where in Shropshire is the world's first cast-iron bridge, built in 1779?

LUDLOW !!!

1 Name one of the two American presidents who had film roles before Ronald Reagan.

2 In 1956, what country did Israeli forces invade in a surprise attack?

3 Which world heavyweight boxing champion retired in 1956, undefeated in 49 fights?

4 In what year was the British Broadcasting Corporation founded: 1919, 1922, 1925, 1926, 1930?

5 Why does the locomotive *Evening Star* have a special place in the affections of railway buffs?

6 In what country is "the lost city of the Incas", which was rediscovered in 1911?

7 In which district of London did serious race riots flare up in September 1958?

8 Which actress has won more Oscars for best actress than anyone else?

9 What major cultural breakthrough was made on American TV's *Hank McCune Show* in 1949?

10 In what year did the Festival of Britain take place as "a gesture of faith in the future"?

11 On what special day should Mardi Gras carnivals properly be held?

12 Which major change to the British jury system was introduced in 1967?

13 What was created when six European countries signed the Treaty of Rome in 1957?

14 Who broke the world record Test match score with 365 not out against Pakistan in 1958?

15 In 1920, how many cars were there in the United States of America: 3, 6, 9, 12 or 15 million?

16 Who was the prime minister of Australia from 1968 to 1971?

17 What elite division of London's Metropolitan Police was formed in September 1920?

18 Television comedy duo Gareth Hale and Norman Pace both used to do what job?

19 In golf, what name is traditionally given to the number three fairway wood club?

20 What limitation did the 22nd Amendment of the US Constitution place on future presidents in 1951?

21 What percentage of the Earth's surface is covered by water: 40, 52, 59, 71, 79?

22 Who played Patrick Bergin's battered, runaway wife in the 1990 movie *Sleeping With The Enemy*?

23 At which London Underground station did a crash kill 35 people when a train hit the buffers in 1975?

24 In 1968, by what name was Czechoslovakia's brief spell of freedom from Russian domination known?

25 Which dashing film hero played by Harrison Ford was named after creator George Lucas' dog?

26 Parts of which two words were combined to make the name "Muppet"?

27 Which European country was the first to give women the vote, in 1906: Denmark, Finland, France, UK?

28 How many barmaids were employed at the Rover's Return before Samantha Failsworth: 12, 17, 23, 30, 35?

29 Name the *Titanic's* sister ship, which made over 500 successful Atlantic crossings.

30 Which animal appropriately features in BBC TV's *The Great Antiques Hunt*?

HIS MIND IS LITERALLY BLANK.

Answers on page 221

Knowall's question:

Who was the hard-hitting Geordie star of *Spender*?

PAUL GASCOIGNE !!!

1. Which TV weather girl is the daughter of a famous Manchester United and England footballer?

2. What is the name of Frank Spencer's long-suffering wife in *Some Mothers Do 'Ave 'Em*?

3. Richard O'Brien and Ed Tudor-Pole have both hosted which mentally and physically challenging game show?

4. Who anchored ITV's gone-but-not-forgotten Saturday sports programme *World of Sport*?

5. In which popular 1980s action series did Hannibal, BA Baracus, Face and Murdock appear?

6. Who played Lady Chatterley's lover in the BBC's 1993 adaptation of the D.H. Lawrence novel?

7. *Who's the Boss* is the American version of which successful British sitcom?

8. Which famous pop star narrated the children's TV version of *Thomas the Tank Engine*?

9. Which runaway black sheep of the Ewing family finished up in *Knots Landing*?

10. Who did Mandy and Beth bury under their garden patio in *Brookside*?

11. Which 1960s TV series about an amiable dolphin was made into a Hollywood film starring Paul Hogan?

12. What is the surname of the family who are depicted in the biting American comedy *Roseanne*?

13. Which famous West Midlands motel was finally demolished by ATV/Central in 1988?

14. Barbara Mandell the first woman to do it on British television in 1955. What?

15. Who replaced Bamber Gascoigne as the host of *University Challenge* on its return in 1994?

16 From which city did incompetent waiter Manuel of *Fawlty Towers* fame originate?

17 Which energetic drama followed the lives of students and staff at a New York performing arts college?

18 Gerald Campion took the title role in the 1950s series featuring which chubby schoolboy?

19 Which member of the royal family appeared on the 200th edition of *A Question of Sport*?

20 How many human survivors are there among the crew of *Red Dwarf*?

21 In which comedy about a traditional department store did John Inman play Mr Humphries?

22 The presenters of which 1960s Friday music show delighted in telling viewers "The weekend starts here"?

23 Name the American who created the absurd animation sequences for *Monty Python's Flying Circus*.

24 Who made his name presenting the improvisational game show *Whose Line Is It Anyway*??

25 According to the commercial, which beer "refreshes the parts other beers cannot reach"?

26 Which satirical Hat Trick production is based in a television newsroom?

27 What car does Rowan Atkinson drive in the television comedy *Mr Bean*?

28 Who played George Cole's bodyguard in the original series of *Minder*?

29 In which American city was the award-winning comedy *Cheers* set?

30 What is the name of the pub frequented by folk from the fictional Yorkshire village of Beckindale?

HE NEVER HITS THE NAIL ON THE HEAD.

Answers on page 221

Knowall's question:

What celebrity charades game featured Liza Goddard and Lionel Blair as captains?

CALL MY BLUFF !!!

1 What is the name of Postman Pat's cat?

2 Who created the hit comedy series *Bread*?

3 In the Channel 4 sitcom, what is Desmond's?

4 Where is the British version of *Gladiators* staged?

5 What was Britain's first ever TV pop music show?

6 Who resides at Crinkley Bottom?

7 How was Dr Richard Kimble also known?

8 What do the letters *M*A*S*H* stand for?

9 Name three of the four *Young Ones* characters.

10 Who was Dick Dastardly's canine companion?

11 Which English comedian journeyed from pole to pole?

12 Zip code 90210 is located where in California?

13 Who chaired *Question Time* from 1979 to 1989?

14 Name Britain's first TV series about a policewoman.

15 Which news review appears daily on Children's BBC?

16 Why was Simon Templar called "The Saint"?

17 Which two satirical performers are "The Long Johns"?

18 In which city is the detective series *Taggart* set?

19 Which two presenters have hosted *This is Your Life*?

20 Who is Fred Flintstone's best friend?

21 At which prison is Helen Hewitt *The Governor*?

22 What rose slowly around Mr Rigsby and Miss Jones?

23 Who lived at 23 Railway Cuttings, East Cheam?

24 Which suave Australian played *Reilly – Ace Of Spies*?

25 What series derived from the one-off play *Woodentop*?

26 In *EastEnders*, who is Bianca Jackson's father?

27 Which unfortunate actor headed the *Police Squad!*?

28 Where was the exotic location of *Magnum PI*?

29 Which couple were *Just Good Friends*?

30 What dodgy business is run by "Del Boy" Trotter?

HE HASN'T GOT A CLUE.

Answers on page 222

Knowall's question:

Name the first horse to belong to Steptoe and Son?

DELILAH !!!

1 What is the name of Eddie's long-suffering daughter in *Absolutely Fabulous*?

2 Detectives Kelly and Sipowicz were partners in which hard-hitting American cop drama?

3 Who hosts *Bullseye*, the quiz show based upon the throwing of "arrows"?

4 Which footballer is married to actress Leslie Ash of *Men Behaving Badly* fame?

5 The final scene in the last episode of the World War 1 comedy *Blackadder Goes Forth* fittingly depicts what?

6 Who starred in *A Man Called Ironside* as a crippled detective chief confined to a wheelchair?

7 How were comedians Newman, Baddiel, Punt and Dennis collectively known?

8 The fictional hospital featured in the BBC's drama *Casualty* is in Holby, but where is it filmed?

9 Which jazz pianist introduces a diverse range of musical acts on his trendy evening show *Later*?

10 What was the name of Ian Richardson's devious politician in the "House of Cards" trilogy?

11 Seymour, Foggy and Blamire are characters from which sentimental BBC comedy?

12 Whose twisted stories inspired the original series of *Tales of the Unexpected*?

13 Which bald, lollipop-sucking New York detective's catchphrase was "Who loves ya, baby"?

14 Which doughty actress is the longest serving member of the *Neighbours* cast?

15 What was the name of Lady Penelope's trusty chauffeur in *Thunderbirds*?

16 Which off-beat travel show is presented by Simon O'Brien and Magenta DeVine?

17 The glamorous beach drama *Baywatch* is set in which sun-soaked American city?

18 What is the relationship between Arkwright and Granville in *Open All Hours*?

19 Who are the disgusting protagonists of the anarchic BBC comedy *Bottom*?

20 Which realistic children's drama about life in a London comprehensive school was devised by Phil Redmond?

21 In what year did *The Benny Hill Show* receive its first television screening: 1955, 1959, 1963, 1967, 1971?

22 To which high-profile lady did Michael Jackson give his first television interview for 14 years in 1993?

23 Who played the lead role in the BBC's classic 1971 biographical drama *Elizabeth R*?

24 In the 1960s, David Jacobs chaired the panel in which review of the week's record releases?

25 Which actor followed in the solid footsteps of William Shatner as captain of the Starship *Enterprise*?

26 Who provided the title for an irreverent sports show during his commentary on the 1966 World Cup final?

27 Which popular quiz was the first-ever programme to be screened by Channel 4?

28 Which smooth-talking host spoke to over 3,000 guests during 1,250 shows between 1985 and 1992?

29 Portmeirion in North Wales was the surreal setting for which 1960s cult series starring Patrick McGoohan?

30 Which Doctor Who went on to appear as the scruffy scarecrow *Worzel Gummidge*?

YE GODS, GIVE ME STRENGTH.

Answers on page 222

Knowall's question:

In *The Sheik* (1921), with which actor does the English heiress played by Agnes Ayres fall in love?

RICHARD BARTHELMESS !!!

1 What was the name of the short, dumpy robot in the *Star Wars* series?

2 In *The Rebel*, Tony Hancock gave up his boring office job to become what?

3 Which film was promoted with the slogan: "Just when you thought it was safe to go back in the water."?

4 The last – and probably the weakest – of the *Carry On* series of films was released in 1992. What was its title?

5 Which western outlaw was the main character in *The Left Handed Gun* and *Young Guns*?

6 What is the name of the character played by Virginia McKenna in the African wildlife epic *Born Free*?

7 Who was Nelson Eddy's female co-star in a series of successful 1930s musical films?

8 Who played the part of Perks the station-master in *The Railway Children*?

9 In *Whistle Down the Wind*, who did the children think the man in the barn was?

10 Which famous composer was portrayed by Gary Oldman in *Immortal Beloved*?

11 What English county was the setting for Joseph Losey's film *The Go-Between*?

12 Who played the mother of Norman Bates in Alfred Hitchcock's *Psycho*?

13 What was the title of the 1986 film about Sid Vicious and his girlfriend Nancy Spungen?

14 What was the name of the planet that astronaut Charlton Heston visited in *Planet of the Apes*?

15 In which of the Beatles' four films does the song *Ticket to Ride* feature?

16 Which hit film of 1995 featured a talking duck named Ferdinand who was desperate to be a cockerel?

17 In the novel, Lolita was aged 12; in the film, she was 14. How old was actress Sue Lyon who played her?

18 What type of large fruit features in a 1996 film of a Roald Dahl children's story?

19 How many times has the classic *A Star is Born* been filmed, most recently in 1976?

20 In what film made in 1989 did Meg Ryan fake an orgasm in a restaurant?

21 Which real-life disaster was the subject of the 1958 film *A Night to Remember*?

22 In which film did Robert De Niro and Al Pacino first appear on screen together?

23 How were Alec Guinness, Peter Sellers, Herbert Lom, Cecil Parker and Danny Green collectively known?

24 According to the lyrics of the title song from *Jailhouse Rock*, what was "Little Joe" blowing on?

25 In the 1976 horror film *The Omen*, with what was David Warner decapitated?

26 Who actually said in a classic western: "A man's got to do what a man's got to do."?

27 In *Casablanca*, how many times does Humphrey Bogart kiss Ingrid Bergman: none, three, five, seven, nine?

28 Don't name *The Magnificent Seven*. Instead, who played the bandit leader?

29 What instrument was played by Marilyn Monroe in *Some Like it Hot*?

30 Name the increasingly frantic tune played by the two banjoists in *Deliverance*.

HE MIGHT AS WELL HAVE SAID A REINDEER.

Answers on page 222

Knowall's question:

Who did Norma Jean Mortenson become?

NORMA SHEARER !!!

1 Harold Abrahams was one of the two "star" runners portrayed in *Chariots of Fire*. Who was the other?

2 What is the opening song in the 1955 Rodgers and Hammerstein musical *Oklahoma*?

3 In the 1952 shocker *Them!*, which insects were turned into giants by atomic radiation?

4 Which Beatle played Private Gripweed in Dick Lester's film *How I Won the War*?

5 What New York district has been mentioned in the titles of two Woody Allen films?

6 What is the name of Scarlett O'Hara's plantation home in *Gone with the Wind*?

7 Which Olympic sport was the subject of *Downhill Racer* starring Robert Redford?

8 Which jazz saxophonist was the subject of *Bird*, directed by Clint Eastwood?

9 Name the two singing stars who appeared with John Wayne in *Rio Bravo*.

10 What 1992 film featured a team of sky-diving Elvis Presley impersonators?

11 In which film did Marilyn Monroe have trouble controlling her dress over a draughty vent?

12 In Disney's *Fantasia*, what piece of music accompanied Mickey Mouse's sequence?

13 What Robert Redford film had this credit line: "No fish were killed or injured during the making of this film."?

14 In which Alfred Hitchcock chase movie was Cary Grant pursued by a crop-dusting plane?

15 In 1992, which animated film featured a character called Jack Skellington?

16   How many sequels did the controversial horror film *The Exorcist* have?

17   Name the robot which featured in the 1956 science fiction movie *Forbidden Planet*.

18   Which 1986 horror film was promoted with the slogan: "Be afraid. Be very afraid."?

19   What distinctive colour were the Meanies in the Beatles cartoon *Yellow Submarine*?

20   How many Von Trapp children did Julie Andrews minister to in *The Sound of Music*?

21   Which of Elvis Presley's many films contained the song *Wooden Heart*?

22   Who played Henry VIII in the Oscar-winning "best picture of 1966", *A Man for All Seasons*?

23   Which film company's logo shows a mountain in front of a circle of stars?

24   Gary Cooper shot three of the gunmen in *High Noon*. Who shot the fourth?

25   In acclaimed film *The Shawshank Redemption*, what was Shawshank?

26   What popular sport was the subject of *Field of Dreams* and *Bull Durham*?

27   Who, inevitably, played Doctor Van Helsing in the classic Hammer horror *Dracula*?

28   What type of headgear is worn by chirpy Jiminy Cricket in Walt Disney's *Pinocchio*?

29   Which sea-faring character has been played by Clark Gable, Marlon Brando and Mel Gibson?

30   What 1982 epic film holds the record for the greatest number of extras ever used in a single scene?

Answers on page 222

Knowall's question:

In which *Doctor* film did Brigitte Bardot appear?

DOCTOR IN LOVE !!!

1 What was the sequel to *The Hustler* starring Paul Newman, made 35 years after the original?

2 What were the cowboys munching round the campfire in *Blazing Saddles*?

3 Akira Kurasawa's *Throne of Blood* was a Japanese version of which Shakespeare play?

4 In which gory film did Arnold Schwarzenegger first say "I'll be back"?

5 How many Fred Astaire and Ginger Rogers musicals were made in colour?

6 On which street was it all too easy to have bad dreams about Freddy Krueger?

7 What Irish rock band in concert took centre stage in the film *Rattle and Hum*?

8 The songs *Spring, Spring, Spring* and *Bless Your Beautiful Hide* come from which musical?

9 Who was the leading lady in Hitchcock's films *Dial 'M' for Murder*, *Rear Window* and *To Catch a Thief*?

10 What distinctive headgear did The Tin Man wear in *The Wizard of Oz*?

11 What Disney cartoon featured a cat called Lucifer and mice called Jaq and Gus?

12 How many years after *Psycho* was the sequel *Psycho 2* released: 2, 8, 17, 23, 27?

13 What was the title of the 1955 film which told the story of jazz great Benny Goodman?

14 In what year was the film *1984* starring Richard Burton actually released?

15 Which film includes the menacing line "Luca Brasi sleeps with the fishes"?

16 During the making of *Jaws*, what nickname did the crew give the mechanical shark?

17 In which 1970 movie do Jean-Paul Belmondo and Alain Delon team up as Marseilles gangsters?

18 The musical *Kiss Me, Kate* was based on which play by William Shakespeare?

19 *Catch Us if you Can* starred which percussive British pop group of the 1960s?

20 How were Michelle Pfeiffer, Cher and Susan Sarandon collectively known in a 1987 film?

21 What's the missing number in the title of this Ed Wood film: *Plan .... from Outer Space*?

22 In John Huston's 1966 epic film *The Bible*, who played the part of Noah?

23 Who sang the theme for the first James Bond film *Doctor No* in 1962?

24 What was the title of the 1956 musical version of *The Philadelphia Story*?

25 Which popular folk singer took the role of Big Daddy in *Cat on a Hot Tin Roof*?

26 Who played Tommy Steele in the film *The Tommy Steele Story*?

27 Alistair Sim starred in what 1951 film based on *A Christmas Carol* by Charles Dickens?

28 Who was the fast lady who drove the bus in the 1994 movie *Speed*?

29 What is the name with which *Annie Hall* star Diane Keaton was christened?

30 Which British rock star appeared in *Merry Christmas Mr Lawrence* and *The Man Who Fell to Earth*?

HE OBVIOUSLY HASN'T SEEN IT.

Answers on page 223

Knowall's question:

What does the Oscar statuette hold in its hands?

A DAGGER !!!

1 What make were the motor-bikes ridden by the two lead characters in *Easy Rider*?

2 Which Swedish actor played the knight in *The Seventh Seal* and a baddie in *Never Say Never Again*?

3 Name two of the three stars of *The Magnificent Seven* who also appeared in *The Great Escape*.

4 What was the title of the first film directed by Mel Gibson, in 1993?

5 In Walt Disney's *Snow White and the Seven Dwarfs*, which dwarf wears specs?

6 Which actor starred with Celia Johnson in the 1946 weepie *Brief Encounter*?

7 Director John Ford claimed to have based what film on a conversation he had with Wyatt Earp?

8 James Dean starred in only three films. How many of them were shot in colour?

9 What country singer appeared with John Wayne in the western *True Grit*?

10 Which explosive performer set fire to his guitar in the concert film *Monterey Pop*?

11 Name the actor who refused to accept an Oscar for his role in *Patton – Lust for Glory*.

12 Who sang *Pinball Wizard* in Ken Russell's 1975 film version of the rock opera *Tommy*?

13 Which French actress starred with weather-beaten Sean Connery in *Shalako*?

14 Which actor has has given his illustrious name to a range of salad dressings and pasta sauces?

15 In *Star Trek III* Captain James T. Kirk's middle name was finally revealed as what?

16 Who won the Oscar as Best Supporting Actor in 1976 for *All the President's Men* and in 1977 for *Julia*?

17 Which British actor is part-owner of trendy London eaterie Langan's Brasserie?

18 In Woody Allen's *Hannah and Her Sisters*, who played the title role of Hannah?

19 How many true "spaghetti westerns" had Clint Eastwood as their star: one, three, five, seven, nine?

20 Which Labour MP has played a nude love scene with the substantial Oliver Reed?

21 Actor Martin Sheen suffered a heart attack during the making of what war film in 1979?

22 Who sang the title song and starred in the 1955 movie *The Tender Trap*?

23 What is the name of the warthog in Disney's epic cartoon *The Lion King*?

24 Husband-and-wife team Humphrey Bogart and Lauren Bacall starred in *Key Largo*, set in what American state?

25 One stage name was Arnold Strong, but what is the real name of macho star Arnold Schwarzenegger?

26 In 1964, who transferred his definitive Professor Higgins from stage to screen in *My Fair Lady*?

27 *Pink Panther* director Blake Edwards is married to which toothsome British actress?

28 Who played the young tearaway who shot dear old P.C. George Dixon in *The Blue Lamp*?

29 Leonard Bernstein wrote the music for *West Side Story*. Who penned the lyrics?

30 In 1969, what became the first X-rated film to win a coveted Best Picture Oscar?

SHARP, BUT SHORT.

DOG

Answers on page 223

Knowall's question:

Movie mogul Sam Goldwyn wasn't always Sam Goldwyn. What was his original name?

GOLDFINGER !!!

1 In the year when *The Sound of Music* was Best Picture, who won Best Actor for *Cat Ballou*?

2 In John Carpenter's film of Stephen King's novel *Christine*, what exactly was Christine?

3 Jimi Hendrix played a distinctive version of American anthem *The Star Spangled Banner* in what film?

4 Which American director and Indian producer are responsible for classics like *The Remains of the Day*?

5 What relation is director Francis Ford Coppola to actor Nicholas Cage?

6 Who played simple Raymond Babbit's long-lost brother in *Rain Man*?

7 Which noisy star of *Rock Around the Clock* was famous for his "kiss curl"?

8 Which composer's music provided the atmospherics for *Death in Venice*?

9 Who won an Oscar for portraying painter Paul Gaugin in *Lust For Life*?

10 Who wrote the music for and acted in Sam Peckinpah's *Pat Garrett and Billy the Kid*?

11 Which keen-eyed observer did Margaret Rutherford play in *Murder at the Gallop* and *Murder Most Foul*?

12 In 1983, which actress and singer made her directorial debut with *Yentl*?

13 Which revered film director appeared as himself in Billy Wilder's *Sunset Boulevard*?

14 In *Robin Hood: Prince of Thieves*, who made a brief appearance as Richard the Lionheart at the end?

15 Which Brit was paid off lavishly after only two years as production chief of Columbia Pictures from 1986?

16 What was the nickname of George Hayes, who played an aged sidekick to Hopalong Cassidy and Roy Rogers?

17 Which movie is the only sequel ever to have won an Oscar for Best Picture?

18 Frenchman Gerard "The Nose" Depardieu made his American debut in 1991. In what film?

19 Which screen icon played the tragic title role in the 1931 film *Mata Hari*?

20 Sales of which item of clothing slumped after Clark Gable removed his shirt in *It Happened One Night*?

21 Which beautifully constructed actress made her debut in *One Million Years BC*?

22 Who played Mr Micawber in the 1934 version of Charles Dickens' *David Copperfield*?

23 Marilyn Monroe was the blonde in *Gentlemen Prefer Blondes*. Who was her disadvantaged brunette co-star?

24 Who provided the distinctive voice for the genie in Disney's *Aladdin*?

25 In what sequel to *True Grit* did John Wayne revisit his role as Marshal Rooster Cogburn?

26 What was the name of megastar Clint Eastwood's father?

27 Steven Spielberg's *Hook* was based on which play by J. M. Barrie?

28 Which Australian opera singer's son plays the lethal Martin Riggs in the *Lethal Weapon* series of films?

29 The westerns *Chato's Land* and *Lawman* were directed by which gourmet Englishman?

30 What 1960s British pop group took its name from the title of a classic John Wayne western?

SOMETHING FISHY THERE.

Answers on page 223

Knowall's question:

Which great performer took the role of Muhammad Ali in *The Greatest?*

SIDNEY POITIER !!!

1 Which American dramatist wrote *The Misfits* as a starring vehicle for his wife?

2 Which actor took over the high-flying film role of Batman from Michael Keaton?

3 In the Walt Disney feature cartoon *Bambi*, what type of creature was Flower?

4 What was the only British musical fim ever to win a Best Picture Oscar?

5 What relevant object is directly beneath the feet of an Oscar statuette?

6 Which confrontational comedian was portrayed by Dustin Hoffman in *Lenny*?

7 Which dynamic duo had an *Excellent Adventure* and a *Bogus Journey*?

8 Name the great singer who sang the soul song *Respect* in *The Blues Brothers*?

9 Who was the character played by Gene Hackman in the two "French Connection" films?

10 Name the only film starring Peter Sellers as Inspector Clouseau that doesn't have "Pink Panther" in the title.

11 Norman Wisdom played a milkman in *The Early Bird*. What was his boss called in the film?

12 Which British songstress of the 1960s was the *Girl on a Motorcycle*?

13 *Little Man Tate* was the first film to be directed by which well-known actress?

14 What cocktail gave its name to a song by The Eagles and film starring Mel Gibson?

15 Who played the sergeant in *Carry On, Sergeant* and went on to become Doctor Who?

16 What sport is the subject of *When Saturday Comes*, starring Sean Bean?

17 In 1936, Louis B. Mayer was told "no Civil War picture ever made a nickel". What film was being discussed?

18 Which one of the performers in *Ghost* won an Oscar in 1991?

19 Name the English actor who played the overweight baddie in *The Maltese Falcon*.

20 Phil Silvers played Sergeant Bilko in the TV series. Who played the character in the later feature film?

21 Which famous movie actress was portrayed in an unfavourable light in *Mommie Dearest*?

22 Which Monty Python film was promoted with the slogan "makes *Ben Hur* look like an epic"?

23 Who played the troubled writer C. S. Lewis in Richard Attenborough's *Shadowlands*?

24 Which famous songwriter was portrayed by Cary Grant in *Night and Day*?

25 In *The Girl Can't Help It* which busty blonde moaned: "Nobody thinks I'm equipped for motherhood."?

26 Which renowned French director had an acting role in *Close Encounters of the Third Kind*?

27 Which actress, once Paul McCartney's girlfriend, seems to have abandoned films for cake-making?

28 Which TV comedy duo made a less-than-successful film debut in *The Boys in Blue*?

29 What was the name of the robot in the 1951 film *The Day the Earth Stood Still*?

30 Who played Fay Wray's role in the 1976 remake of monkey movie *King Kong*?

HE'S GOT FEET OF CLAY.

Answers on page 223

Knowall's question:

Which American producer, Elizabeth Taylor's third husband, was born Avrom Hirsch-Goldenborgen?

RICHARD BURTON !!!

1 What skinny model of the 1960s turned actress of the 1970s had been spotted as Leslie Hornby?

2 Which cryptic early screen comedian wrote under the pseudonym of Mahatma Kane Reeves?

3 What English film actress used one of Henry VIII's wives' names to replace Joyce Frankenberg?

4 J. P. Richardson died in the same plane crash as Buddy Holly. How did the pop world know him?

5 Frances Gumm and Joe Yule Jnr were famous child actors of the 1930s. What were their stage names?

6 While her brother added a second "t" to his surname, Shirley Beaty changed hers to what?

7 Charles Westover had hits with *Runaway, Hats Off To Larry, Swiss Maid* and *Little Town Flirt*. As who?

8 In his early films this hard man of the screen was credited as Charlie Buchinski. What did he become?

9 Father and son actors Martin and Charlie Sheen share the real names of Carlos and Ramon ....?

10 Robert Zimmerman borrowed the first name of a poet and became a folk-rock icon of the 1960s. As whom?

11 What dimple-chinned screen hero went to Hollywood under the guise of Issur Danielovitch Demsky?

12 Plain Brummie Robert Davies adjusted a vegetable name and became a top TV comedian. Who is he?

13 As "Mrs Robinson", Annemarie Italiano famously seduced Dustin Hoffman in 1967. Her stage name?

14 Dianne Belmont's zany behaviour was loved by US TV audiences in the 1950s. What was her name?

15 Some mothers do have them, including Mrs Dumble-Smith giving birth to Michael. Michael who?

16 Declan McManus chose a good Irish surname – but the first one couldn't be more American. What singer?

17 Camille Javal's alliterative screen name became a byword for sex appeal in the 1950s and 1960s. Who?

18 John Eric Bartholomew made a wise move adopting the name of a seaside resort – to become what?

19 Born Terry Nelhams, he always believed in his ability, first as pop star and then as TV actor. Who?

20 Eunice Wayman was hardly the name for a singer of *My Baby Just Cares For Me* (1987). So, what was?

21 Under what name did Nathan Birnbaum become the world's oldest known (and still funny) comedian?

22 Recruited as John Lydon, his name was chosen to fit the rock image created by his manager. What was it?

23 The most successful artist in British pop history is one Harry Webb. How do his millions of fans know him?

24 Apart from Telly Savalas, no one made more money from being bald than Taidje Khan Jnr. Who was he?

25 The leading man of *Scaramouche* fame had the same name as a contemporary Hollywood great. Who?

26 Bernard Jewry became pop singer Shane Fenton, but he had his seven top 10 hits under what exotic name?

27 Which po-faced Hardy partner, born Arthur Jefferson, hedged his bets when he chose his film name?

28 As plain James Smith, he may not have received as much notice singing *Hold Me, Somewhere* or *Maria*.

29 Maurice Micklewhite took his surname from a Bogart film to become one of Britain's biggest stars. Who?

30 She was a heroine to both sides in World War 1, but not as Maria Magdalena von Losch. Who was she?

YOU'RE ON YOUR OWN WITH THIS ONE.

Answers on page 224

Knowall's question:

Who has had top 10 hits with albums entitled *Barry* and *Barry Live in Britain*?

BARRY HUMPHRIES !!!

1 In 1977 who had a hit with the theme song from the film *A Star is Born*?

2 *Moulin Rouge* (1953) was the biggest success in the long career of which popular orchestra?

3 Which actor, better known as a TV cop, had a No.1 in the UK with *Don't Give Up On Us* in 1976?

4 Michael Ball's 1989 hit *Love Changes Everything* came from which Andrew Lloyd Webber musical?

5 Name one of three songs with which Frank Sinatra had No. 1 hits in Britain between 1954 and 1967.

6 Italian tenor Luciano Pavarotti reached No. 2 with which opera favourite hijacked by soccer in 1990?

7 Which blind pianist-composer-arranger played on Nat King Cole's 1962 hit *Let There Be Love*?

8 What former double Righteous Brothers hit took Robson and Jerome to No. 1 in 1995?

9 *Oh Mein Papa* (Oh My Papa) was an instrumental success for which "golden" trumpeter in 1954?

10 *Claire de Lune* is by which French composer whose work was described as "musical Impressionism"?

11 What orchestra conductor was "Manuel" of Manuel and his Music of the Mountains?

12 Which two megastars joined forces on *Don't Let the Sun Go Down on Me* in 1991?

13 Which American singer had UK No. 1 hits in 1959 with *Dream Lover* and *Mack the Knife*?

14 The Ted Heath Orchestra had a hit in the early 1950s with the theme from which television series?

15 Which Welshman had mid-1960s No. 1s with *It's Not Unusual* and *Green Green Grass of Home*?

16 What song from *Sweet Charity* has been associated with Shirley Bassey, despite reaching only No. 21?

17 Who arranged the Scott Joplin piano rag music used in the movie *The Sting*?

18 Doris Day had two No. 1 UK hits in the 1950s. *Secret Love* was one – what was the other?

19 Which ex-Beatle stood at No. 1 for nine weeks in 1977 with a haunting Scottish melody?

20 *Eine Kleine Nachtmusik* has become one of the all-time light classical favourites. Who wrote it?

21 "Look at me, I'm as helpless as a kitten up a tree." What song, by which smooth American balladeer?

22 Which black American singer asked if we knew the way to San José in 1968?

23 Who became a *Stranger in Paradise* at No. 1 in 1955 and later left his heart in San Francisco?

24 Which British singer shot to fame in 1978 by taking the lead role in Andrew Lloyd Webber's *Evita*?

25 What German-Romanian "New Age" duo saw their first two albums reach No. 1 in 1990 and 1994?

26 Patti and Maxine were two of the Andrews Sisters. Who was the third member of the trio?

27 Which Oscar-winning song came from the 1968 film *The Thomas Crown Affair*?

28 What was singing comedian Ken Dodd happily shedding at No. 1 in September 1965?

29 For which instrument did Joaquin Rodrigo compose his popular *Concerto de Aranjuez* in 1939?

30 For which TV series did Enrico Morricone write *Chi Mai*, which made No. 2 in the charts in 1981?

THAT REGISTERS A NEW LOW.

Answers on page 224

Knowall's question:

Who was the toothy lead singer of Herman's Hermits?

BILLY J. KRAMER !!!

1 What was Elvis' first British top 10 hit, in May 1956?

2 Name two original members of Fleetwood Mac.

3 What were the first names of the Everly Brothers?

4 Where did Richard Harris bake a special cake in 1968?

5 In 1967, who first "skipped the light fandango"?

6 Ketty Lester had the original 1962 hit of which song?

7 Which Group kept on running (to No. 1) in 1965?

8 Who's missing: Dave, Dee, Dozy, ..., Mick and Tich?

9 In the 1960s, what was the Stones' recording label?

10 For which Australians was the carnival over in 1965?

11 Who had the first of his 62 top 10 singles in 1958?

12 In 1961, who encouraged us to "jump the broomstick?"

13 Silence proved golden for which group in 1967?

14 Whose 1962 hit *Hey! Baby* was recorded in a garage?

15 Who tinkled to No.1 with *Roulette* in 1959?

16 The first "single" to go straight to No. 1 in Britain was *Here in My Heart,* in 1952. Who was the singer?

17 According to Leonard Cohen in 1968, who "feeds you tea and oranges that come all the way from China"?

18 Who designed the famous album cover for the Beatles' *Sergeant Pepper's Lonely Hearts Club Band* (1967)?

19 Name one of the two singers who in 1957 had UK No. 1s in successive weeks with *Singing the Blues*?

20 When Radio 1 began in 1967, the first record (played by Tony Blackburn) was by The Move. What was it?

21 In 1966, which Jagger-Richards composition took Chris Farlowe and the Thunderbirds to No. 1?

22 Which 1950s star, later killed in road crash, had hits with *Summertime Blues* and *Three Steps to Heaven*?

23 *This Wheel's On Fire* (1968) was later used as the theme music for *Absolutely Fabulous*. Who sang it?

24 Which crooning member of "The Clan" made No.1 in Britain with *Memories Are Made Of This* in 1956?

25 In what year did Joe Cocker take Lennon-McCartney's *With A LIttle Help From My Friends* to No. 1 in Britain?

26 The original line-up of the Supremes comprised Diana Ross, Florence Ballard and which other singer?

27 Which was the first Stones album composed entirely of their songs: *Aftermath, Big Hits* or *Let It Bleed*?

28 In the years 1964-66 only three acts made No. 1 in the album charts: Beatles, Stones and who else?

29 Mitch Mitchell and Noel Redding shared a unique experience with which great rock legend?

30 At the turn of the years 1959/1960, Emile Ford and the Checkmates were at No. 1 in Britain. With what song?

HURRY UP – IT'S ALMOST MIDDAY.

Answers on page 224

Knowall's question:

Who were enjoying "sitting on the beaches, looking at the peaches" in 1977?

THE BEACH BOYS !!!

1 What did Freda Payne have on her hand in 1970?

2 Which comic rode his *Funky Moped* to No. 5 in 1975?

3 Name the creator and manager of the Sex Pistols.

4 Who wrote the lyrics for many early Elton John hits?

5 In 1979, what killed the radio star for Buggles?

6 Who drove his "Chevvy to the levee" in 1972?

7 What instrument did Jethro Tull's Ian Anderson play?

8 Brian and Michael took what "Lowry" song to No. 1?

9 Which duo sang *You're the One That I Want* in 1978?

10 *Twelfth of Never* was a UK No. 1 for which Osmond?

11 Who was *Gonna Make You A Star* in 1974?

12 *Y.M.C.A.* was a big hit for which happy band in 1979?

13 In 1970, where was Norman Greenbaum's "spirit"?

14 Who sang teen anthem *School's Out* in August 1972?

15 Which rocker went *Sailing* to No. 1 in 1975?

16 Which rock band never released a single but had eight consecutive No. 1 albums from 1969 to 1979?

17 Which female star sang with Tamla Motown great Marvin Gaye on *You Are Everything* in 1974?

18 ELO had 15 top 10 hits in the UK between 1972 and 1981. What did the letters abbreviate?

19 The Boomtown Rats' 1979 No. 1 song *I Don't Like Mondays* was written as the result of what event?

20 Name the prehistoric duo who had 11 consecutive top 10 hits between October 1970 and June 1973.

21 Noddy Holder fronted which highly successful Wolverhampton band in the early 1970s?

22 Which British band created a classic rock riff with their 1977 single *Smoke on the Water?*

23 Ozzie Osbourne was the original lead singer with which satanic heavy rock band from 1970?

24 Which artist enjoyed more weeks in the UK album charts than any other act in both 1973 and 1974?

25 What song by Judy Collins re-entered the charts seven times between July 1971 and December 1972?

26 Which group comprised Benny Andersson, Agnetha Faltskog, Anni-Frid Lyngstad and Bjorn Ulvaeus?

27 West Indian group Boney M had two No. 1 hits with "biblical" themes in 1978. Name one of them.

28 What ace Jamaican performer reckoned that *You Can Get It If You Really Want* in 1970?

29 Which large Greek spent more weeks in the British album charts during 1976 than any other performer?

30 Who took *Don't Cry For Me Argentina*, from Andrew Lloyd Webber's *Evita*, to No. 1 in 1977?

COULDN'T YOU JUST THROTTLE HIM?

Answers on page 224

Knowall's question:

Whose 1988 hit *Kiss* was used later as the backing for a mouthwash ad?

MICK JAGGER'S !!!

1 What was George Michael's first No. 1, in 1984?

2 Whose love was tainted in 1981?

3 In 1986, what Duane Eddy re-release made No. 8?

4 Who didn't want to talk about it in 1988?

5 Name Phil Collins' first single after leaving Genesis.

6 Which John Lennon song led in the 1981 New Year?

7 In 1986, who joined Cliff Richard on *Living Doll* Mk 2?

8 Joe Jackson reckoned it's different for who in 1980?

9 Which star's daughter scored with *Kids in America*?

10 Enya burst on the scene in 1988 – with what song?

11 Who shook to 14 top 10 hits between 1981 and 1985?

12 *Belfast Child* was a No. 1 for which big 1980s band?

13 What was Adam and the Ants' arresting 1981 hit?

14 What were we allowed to call Paul Simon in 1986?

15 Survivor's hit *Eye of the Tiger* came from which film?

16 What fruity female vocal group of the 1980s had five "a"s in their name?

17 Which pop star played Wembley and Philadelphia on the same special day in 1985?

18 According to Kirsty MacColl in 1981, where does the guy who "swears he's Elvis" work?

19 Which American female performer topped the charts with *Total Eclipse of the Heart* in 1983?

20 Jennifer Rush proved almost a one-hit wonder with her massive success of 1985. What was the title?

21 *West End Girls* was a debut No. 1 single for which inventive duo in November 1985?

22 Buck's Fizz won the 1981 Eurovision Song Contest and had the first of their three No. 1s with what song?

23 In which American city did the Grunge scene start: Chicago, Los Angeles, Miami, New York, Seattle?

24 What innovative DJ and TV comedian, later to die of Aids, had a top 10 hit with *Snot Rap* in 1983?

25 Which blond British boys had eight consecutive top 10 hits between 1988 and 1989 before fading fast?

26 Which female vocalist had separate top 10 hits in the 1980s with Joe Cocker and Bill Medley?

27 Stevie Wonder's *Happy Birthday* (1981) was a tribute to which murdered American leader?

28 Bryan Ferry had 15 top 10 singles with Roxy Music and on his own, but what was his only No. 1 (1981)?

29 Greek keyboard player Vangelis had single and album hits in 1981 with the music from which film?

30 Odd one out: *One Day in Your Life, Billie Jean, Beat It, I Just Can't Stop Loving You, Black or White?*

NICE TRY, BOYO.

Answers on page 225

Knowall's question:

Who are Bonehead, Guigsy and Tony?

THE THREE DEGREES !!!

1 Which mature rock star won six Grammys in 1993?

2 What was Prodigy's debut single in 1991?

3 For whom could things "only get better" in 1994?

4 What, in 1991, was Iron Maiden's only No. 1 single?

5 Which American rock megastar shot himself in 1994?

6 What US entrepreneur runs the Dreamworks label?

7 What was Prodigy's No. 1 UK album of 1994?

8 Vic Reeves had a No. 1 hit with what song in 1991?

9 In 1992, who were to *Stay* at No. 1 for eight weeks?

10 Who had a big debut hit with *Oh Carolina* in 1993?

11 In 1994, which group were No. 1 at Christmas?

12 What comedy team had a hit with *The Stonk* in 1991?

13 Name one of the Cranberries' first two albums.

14 From which country did Boyzone appear in 1994?

15 Two 1994 hits had titles using one letter. Name either.

16 What 1991 film featured the Bryan Adams song *I Do It For You*, a No. 1 in Britain for 16 weeks.

17 Which television duo's first album outsold their own single, itself the year's topseller, in 1995?

18 Which Blur song won the Brit award for the best single of 1994?

19 What American band signed a record £51 million deal with Warner Bros in August 1996?

20 In 1994, what Danish artist became the first act to go to No. 1 in the first week with a debut single?

21 *Step by Step* shot straight to No. 2 in June 1990 and then moved no higher. Who were the young artists?

22 Who changed his royal name to a symbol in 1994 – and then recorded his first UK No. 1 success?

23 What "condimental" female American duo wanted to talk about sex in the summer of 1991?

24 Which mature rocker had his biggest British hit with the title song of a 1994 movie?

25 Who took the Jim Steinman song *I'd Do Anything For Love* to No. 1 for seven weeks in 1993?

26 Which Wet Wet Wet song, from *Four Weddings and A Funeral*, stayed at No. 1 for 15 weeks in 1994?

27 In the much-hyped battle of the pop groups between Blur and Oasis in 1995, who won the race to No. 1?

28 After four chart-toppers in a row, what band made only No. 3 with *Love Ain't Here Anymore* in 1993?

29 Which 1992 Kevin Costner film featured Whitney Houston's smash hit *I Will Always Love You*?

30 In 1994, who went four places better than the 1981 Diana Ross-Lionel Ritchie version of *Endless Love*?

IT'S NO MIRAGE.

Answers on page 225

Knowall's question:

Which great entertainer collapsed and died on a Madrid golf course in 1977 after winning by one hole?

BOB HOPE !!!

1 Name the radio programme devised by Roy Plomley and presented by him for 44 years.

2 In 1960, the Russians shot down an American U-2 spy plane piloted by whom?

3 Greater London consists of The City of London and how many boroughs: 16, 23, 28, 32, 35?

4 Who was the first woman to be awarded a degree from Oxford University?

5 What was banned on British television screens from 8 February 1965?

6 In what country is the Horn of Africa, the continent's most easterly point?

7 Name the 86-year-old Greek shipping tycoon who died in 1996.

8 Complete this sequence of pre-1971 non-decimal coins: threepenny bit, sixpence, shilling, florin, ...?

9 Who became the first director of Britain's new National Theatre in 1962?

10 In 1996, the most expensive sci-fi film ever made was released and attracted long queues. What was it called?

11 Who was the most prolific British scriptwriter of all time, with over 40 television series to his credit?

12 Which Briton won the women's singles title at the centenary Wimbledon tennis championships in 1977?

13 What was the last item to be freed from rationing after World War 2: butter, clothing, eggs, meat, petrol?

14 Britain's youngest MP was convicted of incitement to riot in 1969 and sentenced to prison. Who was she?

15 Which British model was sued for £330,000 after failing to appear for a Hungarian chat show?

16 Who succeeded Sir Stafford Cripps as chancellor of the exchequer in 1950?

17 Name one of the three American astronauts burned to death in 1967 in their capsule on the launch pad.

18 Which actor played private eye Remington Steele and secret agent James Bond?

19 What fate befell 913 members of the People's Temple religious cult at Guyanan jungle settlement Jonestown?

20 Who starred in the film *10* and refused to appear on television with O. J. Simpson?

21 Which Australian media tycoon set up a cricket "circus" in the 1970s to challenge the official game?

22 By what name is *Fantasy Football League* contributor Angus Loughran better known?

23 Name the England soccer player accused of stealing a gold bracelet in Colombia before the 1970 World Cup.

24 Which of the following does not react with water: calcium, copper, iron, potassium, sodium?

25 Who became president of France in 1974, succeeding the deceased Georges Pompidou?

26 Radio DJ Janice Long is the sister of which energetic Saturday morning TV presenter?

27 To what gruesome lengths were 16 victims of a 1972 plane crash in the Andes driven in order to survive?

28 The mother of which entrepreneur was an air hostess with British South American Airlines?

29 Which radio programme, an afternoon regular since 1922, was dropped by the BBC in 1961?

30 What was the nickname of the 17-year-old American who won the Wimbledon women's singles in 1952?

Answers on page 225

Knowall's question:

Name the Hollywood producer who delivered the delights of soaps such as *Dynasty* and *Beverly Hills 90210.*

CUBBY BROCCOLI !!!

1 In 1996 which country became the first to introduce legislation in an attempt to "censor" the Internet?

2 Who conducted the orchestra in the 1940 animated Walt Disney film *Anastasia*?

3 What did No. 1s *Relax* (Frankie Goes To Hollywood) and *My Ding-A-Ling* (Chuck Berry) have in common?

4 Which leading British designer once owned a shop in partnership with Sex Pistols boss Malcolm MacLaren?

5 How many attempts is a competitor allowed at each height in the high jump?

6 In measuring sound intensity, what unit does 10 decibels equal?

7 Spaghetti, lasagne and tagliatelle are all varieties of which food?

8 How much did Luciano Pavarotti receive for "singin' in the rain" at Hyde Park in 1991?

9 What, unexpectedly, did the Liberal Democratic Party's annual conference of 1995 vote to legalise?

10 Who wrote the lyrics for the Brontë-inspired Cliff Richard musical *Heathcliff*?

11 What breakthrough, valuable in crime detection, did Alec Jeffreys develop in 1985?

12 What was the Dennis Potter television serial in which Bob Hoskins played a sheet music salesman?

13 In which Californian city does the annual Tournament of Roses take place?

14 What were Radio 2, Radio 3 and Radio 4 called before the reorganisation of the BBC in 1967?

15 In 1971 Richard Roundtree starred in a movie best remembered for its music by Isaac Hayes. Name it.

16   When was the driving test introduced in Britain: 1905, 1915, 1925, 1935 or 1945?

17   Which 1960s rock star is buried in the same Paris cemetery as the Polish composer Frédéric Chopin?

18   In the *The Story of Will Rogers,* made in 1952, who played the part of the much-loved US film comedian?

19   In Britain, what is the biggest threat to the future of the red squirrel?

20   What term describes the bending of light as it passes from one medium to another?

21   At which resort on the French Riviera can the *Promenade des Anglais* be found?

22   Name the professor who wrote and presented the ground-breaking TV series *The Ascent of Man?*

23   The largest British county without a university got a privately funded one in 1996. Which county?

24   Who disappeared from his yacht *Lady Ghislaine* off the Canary Islands in 1991?

25   In which year were parking meters introduced to Britain: 1953, 1958, 1963, 1968, 1973?

26   Name the club where Demi Moore worked in the 1996 film *Striptease.*

27   What was the only part of Palestine held in Egyptian hands after the Arab-Israeli War of 1948-49?

28   What is the TV quiz show where extended family teams answer questions on TV programmes?

29   Who was Herman J. Mankiewicz's co-writer on the 1941 classic film *Citizen Kane?*

30   The first name of Colin Dexter's Inspector E. Morse was revealed as what in 1996?

DUBBLE TRUBBLE.

Answers on page 226

Knowall's question:

In 1996 which prominent retired churchman said he had hoped he would die before an embarrassing biography was published?

RODERICK WRIGHT !!!

1 Which Mexican revolutionary leader who finally sued for peace in 1920 was christened Doroteo Atango?

2 Which word is used to describe those plants that can live for many years?

3 In which part of the body are the metacarpals and phalanges found?

4 What aviation "first" was achieved by Charles Kingsford-Smith and C.T.P. Ulm in 1928?

5 Fuel injection for cars was introduced in 1954 by which German engineer?

6 Brandon Thomas was the first-born son of which *Baywatch* star?

7 The slogan "Would you buy a second-hand car from this man?" was coined by Mort Sahl. About whom?

8 In 1996, over £25,000 was paid for the original drawings of what classic British car?

9 What military parade is held in London on the sovereign's official birthday?

10 Which principal dancer with the Royal Ballet starred in Andrew Lloyd Webber's musical *Cats* in 1981?

11 In 1980 the World Health Organisation announced the global eradication of which common disease?

12 Which South Korean car company began selling directly to the British public in 1995?

13 Whose *Letter from America* has been posted to BBC radio every week since 1946?

14 What were the two radical policies adopted by Soviet leader Mikhail Gorbachev after 1985?

15 Name one of the two actresses who played James Herriot's wife in *All Creatures Great and Small.*

16 Which hard-drinking poet's last words were "I've had 18 straight whiskies – I think that's a record."?

17 In 1996 which Billericay MP said: "The way the European Union spends our money is obscene."?

18 What is the name of the largest of the 100 or more Shetland Islands?

19 Name the British thriller writer who created the dashing Bulldog Drummond.

20 Which famous London theatre boasted "we never close" throughout the wartime blitz?

21 Who wrote about her fascinating childhood in Kenya in *The Flame Trees of Thika*?

22 What word is used to describe the process of making discoveries by accident?

23 According to the title of the 1981 film by Bill Forsyth, whose girl was Dorothy?

24 Which company introduced the world's first micro-processor in 1971 and the Pentium chip in 1993?

25 Name the actors who played Bootsie and Snudge in *The Army Game* and later in their own spin-off series.

26 Buddhist monk Talduwe Somerana killed Solomon Bandaranaike in 1959. Of which country was he PM?

27 The first Porsche to be produced was a sports version of which car?

28 In 1971 two important photographic centres opened: one in London and the other in Paris. Name one.

29 Name one of two television series which featured James Arness as US marshal Matt Dillon.

30 At which town in the north-west was Britain's first nuclear submarine built?

Answers on page 226

Knowall's question:

What was unusual about the figure skater who finished second to the great Ulrich Salchow in the 1902 world championships?

HE WORE A BOBBLE HAT !!!

1 Who in 1903 took the first of 1,018 catches in a first-class career that would stretch until 1938?

2 What first tennis "double" did H. L. Doherty, "Little Do" of the famous brothers, achieve in 1902?

3 Which competition was won by "The Wednesday" in 1903 and 1904?

4 Which county won seven cricket championships between 1900 and 1919?

5 Why was Italy's Dorando Pietri presented with a gold cup by Queen Alexandra during the 1908 Olympics?

6 What links the horses Diamond Jubilee, Rock Sand, Pommern, Gay Crusader and Gainsborough?

7 The IIHF was founded in 1908. Of which sport is it the governing body?

8 Which record-breaking opener, later known as The Master, began his Surrey & England career in 1905?

9 What "Good Doctor" became president of the newly formed English Bowls Association in 1903?

10 H. W. Stevenson was world professional champion five times between 1901 and 1911 at which game?

11 Why was the powerboat racing in the 1908 Olympics off the Isle of Wight delayed for nearly two months?

12 In what sport did the British Isles and Australasia contest finals in 1907, 1912 and 1919?

13 What name is given to the Athens Olympics of 1906, held as a result of the mess at St Louis in 1904?

14 What happened after "Gentleman Jim" Corbett k.o.'d "Kid" McCoy in the 6th round in New York in 1900?

15 Which city was scheduled to host the Olympic Games of 1916, cancelled because of World War 1?

16 Which Middlesex and England bowler perfected the googly, taking 132 wickets in the 1905 season?

17 Edward Barrett won two "macho" medals in the 1908 Olympics. One was wrestling – what was the other?

18 Which darling of the racing public was champion jockey for 10 successive years from 1914 to 1923?

19 Who knocked out world heavyweight champion Jack Johnson in the 26th round to take the title in 1915?

20 In which year did the first Tour de France take place: 1900, 1903, 1906, 1909 or 1912?

21 Who became the first £500 British transfer in 1908, and the first £1,000 transfer the following year?

22 Which golfer won five British Opens between 1901 and 1910: James Braid, J. H. Taylor or Harry Vardon?

23 Five times Wimbledon champion, she played hockey for England and won the British golf title (1904). Who?

24 Which German car won the French Grand Prix in 1908 – despite making 11 tyre changes.

25 Why was the 1915 FA Cup final between Sheffield United and Chelsea (3-0) dubbed "the khaki final"?

26 What early rugby league crowd-pleaser scored two tries in the first-ever Test against Australia in 1908?

27 US singles champion in 1909 to 1911, she donated the cup later played for by the US and Britain. Who?

28 He set a world long jump record, played football for England and was captain in six Tests. Who was he?

29 Which Cornish former world heavyweight champion took the new light-heavyweight title in 1903?

30 Which club beat Derby County by a record 6-0 margin in the 1903 FA Cup final at Crystal Palace?

TWO MIGHT HAVE HELPED.

Answers on page 226

Knowall's question:

What was remarkable about Gertrude Ederle's swim across the Channel in 1926, the first by a woman?

SHE SWAM BACKSTROKE !!!

1 At which Surrey track was the first British motor-racing Grand Prix held, in 1926?

2 Which Yorkshireman scored 0 and 1 on his England debut – and a Test record 364 the following year?

3 Who was England's leading flat racing trainer in 1926, the first of six such successes?

4 Which *Chariots of Fire* athlete became manager, official, broadcaster, journalist and statistician?

5 In which year was the FA Cup final first played at Wembley: 1921, 1923, 1925, 1927, 1929?

6 Who was the former Russian prince who scored a brilliant try for England against the All Blacks in 1937?

7 Which Midland county recorded their only success in the cricket county championship in 1936?

8 Who set four track and field world records in just 46 minutes in 1935?

9 What was the name of the original World Cup (1930), presented by the president of the French federation?

10 Walter Hagen's role as 1920s American golf hero was taken by an amateur in the 1930s. Who was he?

11 Which badminton player with a famous surname won all her matches for England from 1926 to 1948?

12 What speed "first" did Gar Wood achieve in his powerboat *Miss America IX* in 1931?

13 Name the "Flying Finn" who won nine Olympic gold medals in distance events in the 1920s.

14 What was the only sport for women at the inaugural British and Empire Games in Canada in 1930?

15 For which baseball team did "Babe" Ruth, legendary hitter of the interwar years, play until 1935?

16 Which manager took both Huddersfield Town (1920s) and Arsenal (1930s) to three League titles?

17 As Kathleen McKane, this English woman won the Wimbledon singles in 1924. How do we know her?

18 Who is the only man to have held the world billiards and world snooker titles at the same time (1928)?

19 In 1930, who scored the first triple century in Tests: Bradman, Hammond, Hobbs, Sandham, Sutcliffe?

20 When did the first Winter Olympics take place at Chamonix, France: 1920, 1924, 1928, 1932, 1936?

21 British lightweight champion in 1934-36, he was later forced to sell his Lonsdale belts to pay debts. Who?

22 What aquatic sport was devised by Ralph Samuelson in Minnesota, USA, in 1922?

23 Which skater won 10 world titles (1927-36) and three Olympic gold medals before going to Hollywood?

24 Well known as the "bodyline" captain, who led the county batting averages in 1927 and 1928?

25 Which woman won the Olympic javelin and hurdles in 1932 and was later triple US Open golf champion?

26 Which of the home national sides had to wait until 1925 for their first rugby union "grand slam"?

27 What tournament was first played at Worcester, Mass. in 1927 for a trophy donated by an Englishman?

28 The first footballer to be knighted, he began his 34-year career with Stoke City in 1931. Who was he?

29 Name the only bowler to take over 300 first-class wickets in a season (304 in 1928)?

30 Which American woman tennis player did not drop a set at Wimbledon between 1927 and 1933?

IT'S JUST A QUESTION OF TIME.

Answers on page 226

Knowall's question:

Which Irish jockey, later to win on Gay Trip in 1970, won his first Grand National on Quare Times in 1955?

JONJO O'NEILL !!!

1 Which bowler dismissed Don Bradman for 0 at The Oval in 1953, leaving him a Test average of 99.94?

2 Name one of the two men who in 1954 helped Roger Bannister break four minutes for the mile.

3 And who was Bannister's great Australian rival who took 1½ seconds off the new record just six weeks later?

4 In 1947, which Scot was the first man to win the world snooker title following the retirement of Joe Davis?

5 Who won the Olympic 100m backstroke in 1956, Britain's first swimming gold medal for 36 years?

6 In American sport, what breakthrough links Kenny Washington (1946) and Jackie Robinson (1947)?

7 Which Derbyshire and England fast bowler topped the county averages in 1953 and 1958?

8 Name the Welsh "gentle giant" who helped Juventus to three Italian League titles in the 1950s.

9 What golfer won a hat-trick of the US Masters, the British Open and the US Open in 1953?

10 Middlesex cricketing brothers Denis and Leslie Compton also played for which London football club?

11 In what year did both the Asian and Pan-American Games begin: 1951, 1953, 1955, 1957 or 1959?

12 Which heavyweight boxing champion holds the record for the longest unbroken reign, from 1937 to 1949?

13 What tennis "first" did "Little Mo", Maureen Connolly, achieve in 1953 at the age of 18?

14 Which Italian football team was decimated by an air crash in 1949: AC Milan, Juventus, Roma or Torino?

15 At what Yorkshire golf course did Great Britain regain the Ryder Cup in 1957 – after a gap of 24 years?

16 Chris Chataway, Gordon Pirie, Jim Laker, Dai Rees, Ian Black, John Surtees. What did they all win?

17 Which Welsh winger, a triple crown winner in 1965, scored a try on his debut against England in 1959?

18 The basic design for what leisure device was set in the 1940s by American scientist Dr Francis Rogallo?

19 What nationality was Juan Fangio, first winner of the world motor racing championship in 1950?

20 Which aptly named Scottish rugby union player helped expand the full-back's role in the late 1950s?

21 Name the British woman who won the world skating title in 1951 and the Olympic gold medal in 1952.

22 Which country won the Davis Cup eight times between 1950 and 1959?

23 What British boxing award was donated by Hugh Cecil Lowther, who died in 1944?

24 Which baseball team appeared in 13 World Series between 1941 and 1958, winning 10 times?

25 New Zealanders won the world speedway title four times in the 1950s with two riders. Name one.

26 Which county won the county cricket championship outright seven consecutive times in the 1950s?

27 What brilliant British racing driver, second youngest winner of a Grand Prix at Spa in 1956, died in 1958?

28 Name the golfer, latterly a TV commentator, who played in eight Ryder Cups and 10 World Cups.

29 What was the horse that collapsed when leading the way home in the 1956 Grand National?

30 Live coverage of which US sport in 1958 revived waning public interest and led to its modern boom?

SOUNDS MORE WELSH TO ME.

Answers on page 227

Knowall's question:

With whom did the Hon. Thomas Robin Valerian Dixon combine to win Winter Olympic gold (1964) and the world title (1965)?

JOHN CURRY !!!

1 Which Scottish runner took a wrong turn in the 1966 Commonwealth Games marathon but still won gold?

2 What horse took David Broome to gold in the 1967 and 1968 European showjumping championships?

3 Jonah Barrington won the British Open squash title from 1967 to 1973, barring 1969. Who won then?

4 The Olympic Games were held for the first time in Asia in 1964. In which city?

5 Which Jamaican-born British weightlifter won world championships in 1959, 1962, 1963 and 1965?

6 Who won four Wimbledon men's singles titles in the 1960s, two as an amateur and two as a pro?

7 Which batsman, in his last Test innings before a car crash ended his Test career, scored 139 not out?

8 Name one of the two British racing drivers who switched to win the Indy 500 in 1965 and 1966.

9 What years marked Arnold Palmer's two victories in the British Open, sparking the UK golf explosion?

10 Jill Hammersley played a record 413 times for England between 1967 and 1983. In which sport?

11 Which New Zealand Test captain set a world best of 15 sixes in an innings for Wellington in 1963?

12 Who was motor cycling's youngest world champion in 1961 and won seven more titles up until 1967?

13 Which cricketer's inclusion in the 1968 squad for South Africa led to the MCC tour being cancelled?

14 Runner of 114 marathons from 1964, his book on distance running is *The Long Hard Road*. Who is he?

15 In what year did Wimbledon finally go "open" to professionals: 1962, 1964, 1966 or 1968?

16 Which pipe-smoking Englishman won the inaugural world bowls championship in 1966?

17 Sister of a famous driver, she took Monte Carlo's Coupe des Dames an 8th time in 1969. Who is she?

18 Who became the first batsman to score 36 off an over in a first-class match for Notts v Glamorgan in 1968?

19 Which British athlete died of cancer in 1970, the year after winning European 800m gold in a record time?

20 Boris Onischenko was disqualified for cheating in the 1976 Olympics. In which section of which event?

21 The best Belgian rider of all time, he won the Tour de France for the fifth time in 1974. Who is he?

22 Which Irish woman won a pentathlon gold medal in the 1972 Olympic Games, held in Munich?

23 English rider Lucinda Prior-Palmer won it four times in the 1970s on four different horses. What event?

24 Which shot-putter, twice Commonwealth No.1 in the 1970s, was also twice the "World's Strongest Man"?

25 David Duckham, Mervyn Davies and Tony Ward all won the player of the year award – in which sport?

26 Why did 32 nations, most of them African, decide to boycott the 1976 Olympic Games in Montreal?

27 Name the Welshman who beat John Lowe to win the first world darts championship in 1978.

28 Which American athlete began his 14-year domination of 400m hurdling in 1976?

29 In 1978, which England cricket captain left the English game to join Kerry Packer's World Series?

30 In which sport did Vasily Alexeyev (USSR) break a total of 80 world records between 1970 and 1977?

I CAN FEEL MY TEETH CLENCHING.

Answers on page 227

Knowall's question:

Which little European nation won the world freshwater angling championships in 1984?

FINLAND !!!

1 Which LA Laker won NBA's Most Valuable Player of the Year award a record sixth time in 1980?

2 Which diminutive Scottish darts player has his best year in 1982, winning world and British Open titles?

3 Eric Heiden won all five speed skating medals in the 1980 Olympics at Lake Placid. What nationality?

4 In 1988-89, who rode 221 winners (in precisely 663 rides) to break the National Hunt record of 149?

5 Which British athlete achieved a world, European and Commonwealth 1,500m treble in 1982-83?

6 Daughter and grand-daughter of speed freaks, who broke the women's water-speed record in 1985?

7 Which woman tennis player took the Grand Slam and the new Olympic singles title in 1988?

8 The 1982 Commonwealth Games 200m produced the only dead heat in top athletics history. Who tied?

9 Which Welshman was sent off in the rugby international against England at Twickenham in 1980?

10 Who won the gold medal for Canada in the super-heavyweight boxing division at Seoul in 1988?

11 The fastest Test hundred was scored (in 56 balls) at Antigua in 1986. By which West Indian batsman?

12 Who became Britain's first judo world champion in 1981 and was five times European champion?

13 Which American broke the four-year European hold on the US Masters by winning in 1992?

14 Who was Steve Redgrave's partner when he won the first of three coxless pairs Olympic gold medals?

15 Which county won the cricket county championship in 1983, 1984, 1986, 1991 and 1992?

16 In which city did Jayne Torvill and Christopher Dean get perfect sixes for artistic impression to take gold?

17 What club won rugby league's Challenge Cup at Wembley every year from 1988 to 1996?

18 In 1997 Ralph Schumacher joins brother Michael on the Formula 1 grid. For which motor racing team?

19 Which blond Kelso farmer won 40 caps at wing-forward for Scotland between 1984 and 1991?

20 Who was Daley Thompson's great West German rival in the pentathlon during the early 1980s?

21 Which country has not won cricket's World Cup since 1983: Australia, England, India, Pakistan, Sri Lanka?

22 Name the British woman javelin thrower voted BBC Sports Personality of the Year in 1987.

23 Which American became the first non-European to win the Tour de France in 1986?

24 In which year were the first World Athletic Championships held: 1983, 1985, 1987, 1989 or 1991?

25 In 1994, which English bowler took 9 for 54 against South Africa at The Oval?

26 Which Swiss city is home to the IOC: Basle, Berne, Geneva, Lausanne, Lucerne or Zurich?

27 Name the Scottish golfer who led the European Order of Merit in 1993, 1994 and 1995.

28 Which ex-League star made his debut for Wasps in a 40-36 win at Union champions Bath in 1996?

29 Which 53-year-old star jockey was seriously injured in a freak accident at Newbury in September 1996?

30 Name the former Australian Test batsman signed to replace Mike Roseberry as Durham captain in 1997.

FABULOUS – 208 WERE CAUGHT.

Answers on page 227

Knowall's question:

Who famously commentated: "He's going for the pink — and for those of you wih black and white sets, the yellow is behind the blue."?

DAVID VINE !!!

1 In 1993, which athlete reckoned: "I'm going to shock the world again, one more time."?

2 Whose dulcet tones gave us: "This would have been Senna's third in a row had he won the two before."

3 "They should send Borg away to another planet. We play tennis...he plays something else." Which rival?

4 Which well-caked voice said: "Dickie Bird, standing there with his neck between his shoulders..."?

5 Who said of two-piece cues: "Alex Higgins hasn't got one because they don't come with instructions."?

6 Which football boss said "...our dressing-room was like Dunkirk before they went over the trenches."?

7 What boxer said: "It's not the size of the dog in the fight that counts, but the size of the fight in the dog."

8 Which Briton, not noted for sporting prowess, said: "Squash — that's not exercise, it's flagellation."?

9 "That will go down in my memory banks as long as I can remember." Which British Open golf winner?

10 "He's without doubt the greatest sweeper in the world. I'd say. At a guess." Which soccer manager?

11 Mike Brearley on whom: "Playing against a team with ? as captain turns a cricket match into gang warfare."?

12 Which boxing promoter said: "I'll shake hands with Bob Arum, but I'll take my ring off first."?

13 Name the rugby league player and coach who observed on TV that "There is no excuse for pace."

14 What astute cricketer and less astute manager said: "I won't say it's easier... but it's easier."?

15 "Oxford is in front! No, Cambridge! No, Oxford! I don't know who's in front – either Oxford or Cambridge!"

16 Which British comedienne: "Jogging is for people who aren't intelligent enough to watch *Breakfast TV*."?

17 "The days of Stirling Moss have gone forever, and long may they continue." Which ex-motoring expert?

18 Which top driver said: "There are two things no man will admit he can't do well – drive and make love."?

19 "Hodge has been unfit for two weeks. Well, no, for fourteen days." Which England football manager?

20 Which deposed England cricket captain retorted: "As one door closes another one slams in your face."?

21 Which bowler said: "David Bryant was giving 101 per cent in effort, which is the least you can ask."?

22 Spot the snooker player: "I need six pints to get to the table, even for a practice."

23 Spot the boxer: "Sure, there have been deaths and injuries in the ring, but none of them serious."

24 Spot the Australian fast bowler: "I enjoy hitting a batsman more than getting him out."

25 Spot the tennis player: "I'm the only woman who doesn't have a sweat problem".

26 Spot the president: "I am still heavyweight champion of Uganda. Nobody is willing to fight me." Really?

27 "I might go to Alcoholics Anonymous, but I think it'd be difficult for me to be anonymous." Which footballer?

28 Which prominent contemporary film comedian once described cricket as "baseball on valium"?

29 Which notorious commentator blustered: "He's even smaller in real life than he is on the track."?

30 Who said: "One of Stephen Hendry's greatest assets is his ability to score when he's playing well."?

SSHHH! KEEP YOUR VOICE DOWN.

Answers on page 228

Knowall's question:

Which nice family man swore repeatedly in a Channel 4 football documentary in 1992?

BRIAN CLOUGH !!!

1 Who succeeded Bob Paisley as the Liverpool manager in 1983?

2 Which country won the Olympic football gold medal in 1912 at Stockholm, beating Denmark 4-2?

3 In 1995-96, which "bunch of lads" came bottom of the Swiss League?

4 Who captained Rangers to their European Cup Winners' success of 1972 against Moscow Dynamo?

5 Which future megastar in Holland and Italy was offered to Arsenal for £200,000 as a 17-year-old?

6 Name the club that played in three FA Cup finals in the 1960s and lost them all?

7 Who scored England's second goal in the 1966 World Cup final: Ball, Charlton, Hunt, Hurst or Peters?

8 Which Scottish club did Chris Waddle join in 1996, scoring in a 2-0 home win on his debut?

9 As Karol Wojtyla, he once played in goal for the Polish amateur side. How is he now best known?

10 Whose penalty was saved by David Seaman to give England victory over Spain in Euro '96?

11 Which Blackpool player was voted the first Footballer of the Year by England's sportswriters in 1948?

12 Name the two Asian countries scheduled to share the hosting of the World Cup in 2002.

13 Who preceded Howard Wilkinson as Leeds manager: Billy Bremner, Allan Clarke or Eddie Gray?

14 Which Soviet club made a crowd-pulling goodwill visit to play London clubs in 1945 after World War 2?

15 Bobby Charlton won two more caps than Bobby Moore, three more than Billy Wright. Give the totals.

16 What nationality is Arsene Wenger, the manager brought from Japan to manage Arsenal in 1996?

17 Hungary trounced England 6-3 at Wembley in 1953. What was the score in the 1954 return in Budapest?

18 Which club clocked up 96 points in gaining promotion from the First Division to the Premier League in 1993?

19 Who scored two goals for Manchester United in the 4-1 European Cup final win over Benfica in 1968?

20 Aston Villa won the first League Cup competition in 1961. Who did they beat in the two-leg final?

21 For which season was the European Cup modified to have two mini-leagues for the last eight clubs?

22 Who, in 1984, became the first British player to win the Golden Boot as Europe's highest league scorer?

23 Of the 15 World Cup final competitions, which has produced the highest average attendance (68,604)?

24 Which side replaced Bayern Munich in the 1974 World Club Championship and beat Independiente?

25 Which side had four players sent off against Rangers in the Premier League in September 1996?

26 Name the player who won cup winner's medals in England, Scotland and Northern Ireland.

27 Which club beat Terry Venables' Barcelona to win the European Cup final at Seville in 1986?

28 By what score did Uruguay beat Scotland at Basle in the 1954 World Cup finals?

29 What country beat Tunisia 2-0 to win the African Nations Cup for the first time in January 1996?

30 Which English club were known as Small Heath until 1905 and added City to their name in 1945?

Answers on page 228

Knowall's question:

Name the mongrel that found the Jules Rimet Trophy abandoned in a South London hedge on the eve of the 1966 World Cup finals.

BONZO !!!

1 Which modest, unassuming former England player (59 caps) was caught for speeding in 1996?

2 Joe Bambrick scored a British record six goals for N. Ireland against Wales in 1930. What was his club?

3 Which country reached the World Cup final in 1974 and 1978 – and lost them both?

4 Who scored the First Division play-off winner against Crystal Palace in 1996 to gain Leicester promotion?

5 Which England player's four moves between July 1991 and July 1995 totalled nearly £22 million?

6 In what year did both Wales and Northern Ireland make the last eight of the World Cup finals?

7 Which was the first club in Britain to install artificial turf on their ground (1981)?

8 Who in 1995 became the first non-European to win the European Footballer of the Year award?

9 Who in 1994 became the first non-Scot to win the Scottish Footballer of the Year award?

10 Real Madrid won the first European Cup final in 1956. Which side did they beat 4-3 in Paris?

11 Which club recorded the highest average home gate in the First Division in 1995-96 (24,786)?

12 Name the Dutch substitute whose Wembley goal stopped Scotland making the last eight in Euro '96.

13 Which club won the Vauxhall Conference by nine points in 1996 but didn't make the Football League?

14 Who scored seven goals for Man. City against Luton in Jan. 1961 and still finished on the losing side?

15 Which club won the South American Cup in 1995 but lost the world title to Ajax on penalties in Tokyo?

16 Poland's 1973 Wembley downer. Hand of God goal in Mexico. German parabola in Italy. What's the link?

17 Who scored three in Newcastle's 6-2 aggregate win over Ujpest Dozsa in the 1969 Fairs Cup final?

18 What name is missing: Winterbottom, Ramsey, Revie, Greenwood, Robson, Taylor, Venables, Hoddle?

19 Real Madrid have won the European Cup a record six times. Which club comes next, with five wins?

20 What do Albion, Blackburn, Bristol, Doncaster, Raith and Tranmere have in common?

21 Who was the Haitian-born US player who scored the goal that beat England in the 1950 World Cup finals?

22 Name the players (Dutch, French, Dutch) who have been European Footballer of the Year three times?

23 Before Liverpool's hat-trick of 1982-84, who last won three consecutive Football League titles, and when?

24 Who was the Scotland manager when they beat England 3-2 at Wembley in April 1967?

25 Which British club beat Atlético Madrid 5-1 in 1963 to become the first to win a European trophy?

26 Which veteran striker led the First Division League scorers in 1995-96?

27 Name one of the two clubs involved in Britain's first £10,000 transfer, of David Jack, in 1928?

28 In 1996 there were two Nigerian international strikers playing in the Premier League. Name one.

29 In what year were the North and South sections of Division 3 abolished and Division 4 created?

30 Who comes next: Alan Shearer, David Platt, Stuart Pearce, Paul Gascoigne, Teddy Sheringham?

HE KNOWS HIS ONIONS.

Answers on page 228

Knowall's question:

What was unusual about Stanislawa Walasiewicz, winner of the women's Olympic 100 metres in 1932?

SHE WAS A POLE VAULTER !!!

1 Billy Mills, the Sioux Indian who won the 10,000 metres in 1964, was the subject of which 1966 film?

2 In what sport did Denmark's Paul Elvström appear in seven Games, winning four consecutive gold medals?

3 Which Soviet athlete won the men's sprint double at the Munich Olympic Games in 1972?

4 The youngest Olympic gold medallist was American Marjorie Gestring (13), in 1936. In which sport?

5 What was the (extremely long) name of the boat captained to gold by Rodney Pattison in 1968?

6 Name the Russian who completed the 5,000 and 10,000 metres double at Melbourne in 1956.

7 In what event did Steve Redgrave win the first of his four rowing gold medals in 1984?

8 What links Lord Burghley (1928), David Hemery (1968) and Sally Gunnell (1992)?

9 In which year was judo introduced into the Olympic schedule: 1964, 1968, 1972, 1976 or 1980?

10 In 1972, what was significant about the victory by West Germany's Liselott Linsenhoff in the dressage?

11 Which small Norwegian town hosted the Winter Olympics in 1994?

12 Where did Britain finish in the Paralympic Games medals table at Atlanta in 1996: 2nd, 4th, 6th or 8th?

13 What was special about the victory of Joan Benoit (USA) in the 1984 women's marathon?

14 Which Manchester United manager took charge of Great Britain's soccer team in the 1948 Games?

15 Which Australian athlete broke the world record in taking the men's 1,500 metres gold medal in 1960?

16 Five-time Tour de France winner Miguel Indurain took the road race at Atlanta in 1996. For whom?

17 Who created Olympic history with a phenomenal 5,000/10,000 metres double in 1972 and 1976?

18 Name two of the three cities that have twice hosted the modern Olympic Games.

19 Which favourite's golden chance in the 3,000 metres of 1984 ended after she collided with Zola Budd?

20 Showjumper Raimondo d'Inzeo made a record eight appearances in the Olympics. For what country?

21 Which city came second to Sydney in the vote for hosting the Olympic Games in the year 2000?

22 Where did Britain finish in the medals table at the Barcelona Games of 1992: 9th, 13th, 17th or 21st?

23 At which Games were 11 members of the Israeli team murdered by Palestinian terrorists?

24 Which future world heavyweight boxing champion won an Olympic gold medal at Mexico City in 1968?

25 In Berlin in 1936, who blew Hitler's theories of "white supremacy" by winning four athletics gold medals?

26 What was special about Sweden's Oscar Swahn, who won the single-shot running deer shooting in 1908?

27 In which Japanese city were the Winter Olympics first held outside Europe or the USA, in 1972?

28 How many events were there in the 1904 Games at St Louis: 10, 100, 200, 300 or 400?

29 What was the eminently forgettable mascot of the 1996 games, paraded first at Barcelona's closing ceremony?

30 Name the French athlete who won both the women's 200 and 400 metres at the Atlanta Games in 1996.

Answers on page 229

Knowall's question:

What is Daley Thompson's first name?

DALEY !!!

1 Name the first Englishman to take 300 Test wickets.

2 Which boxer was billed as "The Dark Destroyer"?

3 Who cost Sir John Hall £15 million in 1996?

4 In what did Chris Brasher win Olympic gold in 1956?

5 Who was world 500cc motor-cycle champion 1976-77?

6 Who won a bronze medal in the heptathlon at Atlanta?

7 In 1947, which jockey had most wins in a "flat" season?

8 Who was the last Briton to win the Wimbledon singles?

9 Who won the javelin in the 1990 European finals?

10 Which pair won four world ice-dancing titles in a row?

11 Name Britain's last European Footballer of the Year.

12 Who was the last British boxer to win Olympic gold?

13 Which Welsh wizard won the US Masters in 1991?

14 Who was world decathlon champion in 1983?

15 Who was world rally champion in 1995?

16 Who in 1992 became the first British woman to win an Olympic track medal since Ann Packer in 1964?

17 Who is the odd man out: Hawthorn, Moss, Hill, Surtees, Clark, Stewart, Hunt, Mansell?

18 Which country did Britain beat in the final of the Olympic hockey in Seoul in 1988?

19 England v Australia at Headingley in 1981 is seen as Ian Botham's match, but who took a Test best of 8-43?

20 Name the lad who cried at the Barcelona Olympics before being thrown into the water by the Searles?

21 Which No. 5 seed did Tim Henman beat in the first round of the men's singles at Wimbledon in 1996?

22 Which present county and Test umpire scored a century on his Test debut at Lord's in 1969?

23 The Lance Todd Trophy is awarded to the "man of the match" after which annual fixture?

24 Which two British athletes won gold medals in the same field event at the Tokyo Olympics in 1964?

25 Which famous Welsh rugby union scrum-half became the youngest captain of his country at 20?

26 Who partnered Tim Henman to a silver medal in the men's tennis doubles at the 1996 Olympics?

27 Who scored 364 for England against Australia at The Oval in 1938, a Test record that stood for 20 years?

28 Which Briton succeeded John Curry as Olympic figure-skating champion in Moscow in 1980?

29 Which player holds the record for the number of tries scored for England at rugby union?

30 Brian Barnes defeated which great American golfer twice in one day during the 1975 Ryder Cup?

Answers on page 229

Knowall's question:

The Louisiana Superdome is the home stadium of which NFL team?

THE ST LOUIS CARDINALS !!!

1 Which is the only team ever to achieve a perfect record in a Superbowl season?

2 The first baseball World Series was held in 1903, but which two teams competed?

3 Who was the first man to complete an Olympic gold-medal double at 200 and 400 metres?

4 Which North American city is home to the Cubs, the Bears and the Blackhawks?

5 Who signed an eight-year contract worth $48 million with the Dallas Cowboys in 1996?

6 Which smartly dressed American golfer always plays tournaments in the colours of teams from the NFL?

7 What is the name of the annual award given to the top American college footballer?

8 Who is the youngest-ever fighter to have become heavyweight boxing champion of the world?

9 Which ice hockey team has won the coveted Stanley Cup more times than any other?

10 What event takes place annually on the first Saturday in May at Churchill Downs, Louisville?

11 By what process do professional American sports teams acquire the majority of their players?

12 In which motor sport does Al Unser Jnr compete against Michael Andretti?

13 Who surpassed Babe Ruth's long-standing record when he hit his 715th home run in 1974?

14 Which legendary quarterback led the San Francisco 49-ers to four Superbowls between 1982 and 1990?

15 In 1996, what great advantage did basketball player Gheorg Muresan have over opponents?

16 Name the sport in which Lance Armstrong competes for America.

17 The Daytona 500 race is the premier event of the NASCAR season. What does NASCAR stand for?

18 What was unusual about the purchase of Honus Wagner for $451,000 in 1991?

19 To which city did the Los Angeles Raiders return at the beginning of the 1995-96 season?

20 Which American athlete broke Daley Thompson's world record for the decathlon?

21 Which basketball "great" made a sensational return from retirement in 1996?

22 Which phenomenal baseball star died of a disease which later took his name?

23 A jagged bolt of lightning is the distinctive emblem of which NFL team?

24 How many points is each converted shot from the free-throw line worth in basketball?

25 Which former England goalkeeper joined American soccer team The Colorado Rapids in 1996?

26 The scandal involving Tonya Harding brought notoriety to which graceful sport?

27 Which sporting event in New York frequently attracts crowds in excess of two million?

28 By what name are the American rugby union team more commonly known?

29 What fundamental amendment to the rules of American Football was made in 1906?

30 Name the four different conferences in which sides from the NBA compete.

ONE OF THESE DAYS HE'LL BE CANONISED.

Answers on page 229

Knowall's question:

London's busiest streetwalker,
Phyllis Pearsall, died in 1996.
Who was she?

A METER
MAID !!!

1 Who was the Democratic candidate beaten by Richard Nixon in the presidential election of 1968?

2 In what year was the "three-day week" introduced by the government in Britain?

3 Which famous actress, referring to her premature retirement, said "I have made enough faces."?

4 Which 1994 album from the Rolling Stones was their first No. 1 in the UK for 14 years?

5 Which British car company produced the Kitten, Rebel, Robin, Sabre and Scimitar?

6 Who was the sharp character played by Orson Welles in the 1949 movie *The Third Man*?

7 By what more familiar name is the spiritual leader Tenzin Gyatso generally known?

8 A third of which western county could be under water by 2030 if present levels of global warming continue?

9 What is the name most frequently chosen by Popes: Benedict, Gregory, John or Paul?

10 In 1996, which well-known high street name reported a trading loss for the first time in its 204-year history?

11 When was third-class travel abolished on railways in Britain: 1926, 1936, 1946, 1956, 1966 or 1976?

12 Name the family who owned the Ponderosa ranch in the long-running television western series *Bonanza*.

13 In which modern country may the ruins of ancient Carthage be found?

14 Name two of the four British boxers who fought Muhammad Ali for the world heavyweight title.

15 In what year was Britain's currency converted to the decimal system?

16 What was the oil tanker that caused serious pollution after running aground in Pembrokeshire in 1995?

17 In 1996 which British soap's former character made a brief return to advertise reruns on satellite TV?

18 Lev Bronstein was a revolutionary Russian who was murdered by Soviet agents. What name did he adopt?

19 Whose belated Broadway debut, in *Sunset Boulevard* in 1996, drew rave reviews from the New York critics?

20 What decision caused chaos in the British money markets on 18 September 1992?

21 Which highly successful Australian tennis pair of the 1990s are known as the "Woodies"?

22 The Royal Shakespeare Company was founded in 1969. Who was its first director?

23 What was the codename of the *Washington Post*'s informant during the Watergate scandal of 1973?

24 In terms of titles, what links *the Pink Panther* (1974), *the Jedi* (1983) and *the Living Dead* (1984)?

25 Who were the miserable radio family made famous on the BBC comedy programme *Take It From Here?*

26 How long did the General Strike of 1926 last: 9 days, 29 days, 49 days, 69 days, 89 days or 109 days?

27 Which South American countries fought the Chaco War of 1932-35, settled by arbitration in 1938?

28 Name the store employing Mr Humphries, Miss Brahms and Mrs Slocombe in *Are You Being Served?*

29 Which 1950s American radio DJ probably coined – and certainly popularised – the phrase "rock 'n' roll"?

30 In which year did unemployment in postwar Britain hit 3 million for the first time: 1976, 1978, 1980 or 1982?

HE GETS COMPLETELY LOST SOMETIMES.

Answers on page 230

Knowall's question:

People described as ectomorphic are what?

HANDSOME ???

1 The Jew's House, National Cycle Museum and Usher Gallery are in which British city?

2 The CGC now ranks second to the Victoria Cross for bravery. What do the letters stand for?

3 Between them, two Michael Jackson albums spent 188 weeks in the charts in the 1980s. Name one.

4 Which village near Bradford, used as the setting for *Emmerdale*, was threatened with the axe in 1996?

5 In which team game are the positions "first defence", "in home" and "second attack"?

6 Which actress, christened Shirley Schrift, won Oscars for *The Diary of Anne Frank* and *A Patch of Blue*?

7 What spoof version of *The Maltese Falcon* made in 1975 starred George Segal as Sam Spade Jnr?

8 Which former actor was the first director of the replica Globe Theatre, which opened in 1996?

9 Manuel Benitez was one of the greatest matadors in bullfighting history. What was his professional name?

10 Who disappeared from LBC Radio and appeared as the quiz-master of *Blockbusters* and *Raise the Roof*?

11 In 1996, which American singer sued former members of his group for "stealing" (half) the band's name?

12 Which Marx brother said: "I'll bet your father spent the first year of your life throwing rocks at the stork."?

13 What ground-breaking photo-journalistic magazine was first published in the USA in 1938?

14 The award-winning airline Cathay Pacific operates out of which centre in Asia?

15 In a television advertisement for what glamorous tipple did Leonard Rossiter pour a drink over Joan Collins?

16 What was the nickname of the 7th Armoured Division, famed for action in North Africa during World War 2?

17 Which classic Hollywood drawler said of acting: "Talk low, talk slow and don't say too much."

18 A marriage that has lasted for 70 years is described by what phrase?

19 In 1918 a common disease killed over 17 million people in India. What was it?

20 Which now-deceased TV presenter said: "There was life before *Coronation Street*, but it didn't add up to much."?

21 In which year did Mao Tse-tung declare the Communist People's Republic of China?

22 What title was taken by Anthony Armstrong-Jones, photographer husband of Princess Margaret?

23 Who gracefully retired in 1908 having scored 54,896 runs and taken 2,876 wickets in first-class cricket?

24 What nautical record was broken by *Hoverspeed Great Britain*, a wave-cutting catamaran, in 1990?

25 Which Socialist weekly did Michael Foot, later leader of the Labour Party, edit for nine years?

26 Whose 1994 hit *You Don't Love Me (No, No, No)* was used by Nissan for their advertising campaign?

27 Sailing due west from Land's End and maintaining the same latitude, which country is reached first?

28 What city was the setting for *The French Connection*: Chicago, Dallas, Los Angeles, Miami or New York?

29 In which year did Soviet troops finally withdraw from Afghanistan: 1983, 1985, 1987, 1989 or 1991?

30 From which 1968 sci-fi film starring Jane Fonda did 1980s group Duran Duran derive their name?

HE'S GOING SKINNY DIPPING.

Answers on page 230

Knowall's question:

Who was Master of the Queen's Music from 1953 to 1975?

SIR MALCOLM SARGENT !!!

1 The first rock musical made its debut in 1967 with the dawning of the "Age of Aquarius". What was it?

2 In 1996 police found three dead bodies in the deep freezer of a Lebanese restaurant. In which city?

3 Which camp "Carry On" favourite played Rambling Syd Rumpole in *Round the Horne* on 1950s radio?

4 What educational construction kit for children was introduced by Frank Hornby in 1907?

5 What two rivers gave their names to the "line" that divided Germany and Poland after World War 2?

6 Name the Australian broadcaster and *Daily Mirror* writer who campaigns against international injustice.

7 What futuristic aid for golfers was introduced at wealthy American clubs in the USA in 1996?

8 What do the letters ACS convey after a name on the credits of a film?

9 What was the name of the dog that accompanied Enid Blyton's *Famous Five* on their adventures?

10 John Major's wife Norma was employed as a teacher for six years. What was her subject?

11 In which country can you find Europe's only wild bison: Albania, Poland, Romania, Russia, Sweden?

12 Which film ends with the words "Oh Aunt Em, there's no place like home", and who spoke them?

13 What party lost the deposit in all 253 seats it contested in the 1992 general election?

14 Which Italian heavyweight boxing champion appeared as an actor in the film *On The Waterfront*?

15 What year of the modern "Troubles" were British troops deployed in Northern Ireland: 1967, 1969, 1971, 1973?

16 Name the officer in charge of the scruffy Home Guard outfit in television's *Dad's Army*, played by Arthur Lowe.

17 Why was a spice-packing factory at Corby in Northamptonshire closed down in 1995?

18 How did the Desilu studio in Hollywood, a source of TV programmes from the 1950s, get its name?

19 Which member of the royal family died in a plane crash in August 1972?

20 Why did Frederico Fellini choose the title *8½* for his extravagant film of 1963 starring Marcello Mastroianni?

21 What links a character from the Wombles, a hit by Irish singer Enya and a South American river?

22 What is the minimum age an American president must be in order to take office?

23 Which African country comes next: Gabon, Congo, Zaire, Uganda, Kenya, ... ?

24 In which drinking club do Arthur Daley and Terry McCann pass the time of day in *Minder*?

25 What date was referred to by US President Franklin Roosevelt as "a day that will live in infamy"?

26 Who died in 1989 having given voices to Bugs Bunny, Daffy Duck, Tweety Pie and many other characters?

27 In which country is the ruined "temple city" of Anghor Wat, the world's biggest religious complex?

28 Which year saw Japanese car production overtake that of the US: 1968, 1972, 1976, 1980 or 1984?

29 Which US state has the largest areas of land allocated to the American Indians?

30 It seems unlikely, but Marlon Brando and Doris Day have something intimate in common. What is it?

SHEER IGNORANCE.

Answers on page 230

ANSWERS

Quiz 1

**Knowall's answer:
Sherlock Holmes (in over
200 films by more than 70
actors)**

1. General Certificate of
   Secondary Education
2. North and South Korea
3. Anne
4. The Perishers
5. Penicillin, discovered in
   1928
6. The sperm whale
7. 1939
8. Justice of the Peace
9. Short-sightedness
10. Christian Dior
11. 1983
12. Architect
13. Montana
14. Sharron Davies
15. Corporation tax
16. The one with the
    longest unbroken
    service as an MP
17. *The Elephant Man*
18. Betamax
19. The Rovers Return

20. 1996
21. (Oliver) Mellors
22. Lenin and Trotsky
23. Donald Campbell
24. Carlos the Jackal
25. Joan Bakewell
26. Harley-Davidson
27. 26
28. Cochineal
29. Helen Keller
30. The Victoria Cross, for
    bravery in the Falklands
    War

Quiz 2

**Knowall's answer:
Springfield**

1. Read Only Memory
2. District of Columbia
3. Rugby union
4. Yellow
5. Charles de Gaulle
6. Hungarian Laszlo Biro
7. "Lurch" (Ted Cassidy)
8. George Bernard Shaw
9. From the initials of its
   founder, T. E. S. Cohen
10. Debbie Reynolds
11. Milwaukee, Wisconsin
12. On the Moon: it was a
    No. 1 single in the UK
13. A Great Dane
14. The Pope
15. Brian Johnston
16. The kipper tie
17. Radio Luxembourg
18. Brandy
19. *Art deco*
20. Sri Lanka
21. British Overseas
    Airways Corporation
22. Liverpool
23. Russia

24. Ian Fleming, creator of
    James Bond
25. Milton Keynes
26. Marc Dutroux
27. British Guiana
28. Woodford
29. Middlesbrough and
    Sunderland
30. BBC boxing
    commentator Harry
    Carpenter

Quiz 3

**Knowall's answer: In a
garden (Camilla Parker-
Bowles' garden)**

1. Mothercare
2. Kiri Te Kanawa
3. Harvard
4. Bobby Moore
5. *The Poseidon Adventure*
6. Steve Ovett
7. Russ Abbot
8. Gary
9. The juke box
10. Jessica
11. He accused Michael
    Jackson of molesting
    him
12. Max (Lionel Stander)
13. Sir Michael Redgrave
14. The world's first Boy
    Scout rally
15. King Hussein of Jordan
16. 1928 (Amsterdam)
17. *The Sweeney*
18. John McCarthy
19. 1988
20. *Jurassic Park*
21. Wapping
22. 1990
23. *The Sunday Times*
24. One in 80

25. Russian President
    Boris Yeltsin
26. They all became
    successful musicals
    (*Fiddler on the Roof,
    Cabaret, My Fair Lady,
    Carousel, Hello Dolly*)
27. Roy Hattersley
28. Divine Brown (famous
    for her brief encounter
    with actor Hugh Grant)
29. Mr Spock in *Star Trek*
30. Benjamin Britten

Quiz 4

**Knowall's answer: Alfred
Lord Tennyson**

1. He was a stockbroker
2. The *Terra Nova*
3. Queen Victoria
4. Selfridge's
5. Japan's
6. The New York subway
   opened
7. The Automobile
   Association
8. Oklahoma and New
   Mexico
9. Emile Zola
10. Theodore Roosevelt
11. Egypt, the Aswan dam
12. US President William
    McKinley
13. Lake Constance
    (Bodensee)
14. The Quantum Theory
15. The Palace of Knossos
16. Ernest Rutherford
17. The Dreadnought
    battleship
18. The Boy Scouts
19. The Thuggees
20. It went onto the gold

standard
21. Louis
22. White City
23. Ivan Pavlov
24. Pearl Harbor
25. Emmeline Pankhurst
26. Mt Vesuvius
27. The *Potemkin*
28. Mohandas Gandhi
29. Anton Chekhov
30. Aspirin

Quiz 5

Knowall's answer:
Hugo Junkers
 1. Newmarket
 2. The Red Cross
 3. Mary Pickford, Charlie Chaplin, Douglas Fairbanks, D. W. Griffith
 4. Its absolute right to veto legislation
 5. Sidney Street
 6. "Red Rosa" Luxemburg
 7. Fly the Atlantic
 8. Lord Kitchener
 9. Scapa Flow, Orkneys
10. Olympia
11. Grand Central Station
12. The Royal Flying Corps
13. Liberals and Tories
14. Journalist
15. Winston Churchill
16. St Paul's Cathedral
17. Weimar
18. The Spirit of Ecstacy
19. Italy
20. The Keystone Cops
21. 1918
22. Porfirio Diaz
23. The tango and two-step
24. Germany and Russia

25. Alsace-Lorraine
26. Lenin and Trotsky
27. Sir Edward Carson
28. The Easter Rising
29. The Chequers Estate
30. Cocaine

Quiz 6

Knowall's answer:
Charles Darwin's "natural selection" theory
 1. Adolf Hitler
 2. "Black Thursday" (24 October)
 3. The vote
 4. £1 and 10 shilling notes
 5. Germany's war reparation payment
 6. The R-101
 7. The Irish Free State
 8. Cricket's "Ashes"
 9. Amelia Earhart
10. Lenin
11. Public telephone boxes
12. The Duke of York (later George VI)
13. Annual "Oscar" awards
14. Roald Amundsen
15. A homeland in Palestine
16. 10/- (50p)

17. The Ottoman Empire
18. Queen Alexandra
19. Tintin
20. The League of Nations
21. Malcolm Campbell
22. The Flying Doctor service
23. Saudi Arabia
24. 200 billion marks
25. *The Spirit of St Louis*
26. The Charleston
27. Yugoslavia
28. Jaguar
29. 355,461
30. A total eclipse of the Sun

Quiz 7

Knowall's answer:
Lord Beaverbrook
 1. 3 September 1939
 2. Jarrow
 3. Adolf Hitler
 4. Emperor Haile Selassie
 5. The River Plate
 6. Jack Hobbs
 7. Paul von Hindenburg
 8. Japan
 9. The "Pact of Steel"
10. Edgar Wallace
11. The Rhineland
12. Edward VIII (before abdicating)
13. T. E. Lawrence (of Arabia)
14. The Spanish Civil War
15. The World's Fair
16. Guernica
17. Albania
18. Gatwick
19. Bruno Hauptmann
20. George Gershwin
21. Major Ramon Franco
22. A "New Deal"

23. Italy's Benito Mussolini
24. Heinrich Himmler
25. Sir Oswald Mosley
26. The *Royal Oak*
27. Edward Elgar
28. Stanley Baldwin
29. Hitler and Stalin
30. Pinewood

Quiz 8

Knowall's answer:
Winston Churchill
 1. Ronald Reagan
 2. The "prefab"
 3. Finland
 4. Colonel Juan Perón
 5. Unity Mitford
 6. He leaked his own Budget secrets
 7. Rudolf Hess
 8. *The Great Dictator*
 9. 55 million
10. Lidice
11. Eamon de Valera
12. 7 May 1945
13. Sicily
14. Edinburgh
15. The Berlin Airlift
16. *Whisky Galore*
17. India
18. From injuries received in a car crash
19. Chiang Kai-shek
20. Burnden Park, Bolton
21. First to break the sound barrier
22. The Iron Curtain
23. Konrad Adenauer
24. The *Exodus 47*
25. The *Daily Mirror*
26. General Wladislaw Sikorski
27. The Battle of the Bulge

ANSWERS

28. Harold Wilson
29. The North Atlantic Treaty Organisation (NATO)
30. Donald Bradman

Quiz 9

Knowall's answer: Bill Haley and the Comets

1. General Charles de Gaulle
2. Austin and Morris
3. Blackpool
4. Albert Einstein
5. The Stone of Scone (Coronation Stone)
6. Eva Perón
7. The Warsaw Pact
8. Charlie Chaplin
9. The "Mau Mau"
10. 1954
11. Richard Nixon
12. Devon Loch
13. Elvis Presley
14. Stirling Moss
15. Myxomatosis
16. Treetops Hotel, Kenya
17. Anaheim, California
18. An American H-bomb test
19. 1955
20. General Douglas MacArthur
21. John Cobb
22. Frank Sinatra
23. Le Mans
24. Melbourne (1956)
25. Archbishop Makarios
26. Michael Bentine (briefly), Spike Milligan, Harry Secombe, Peter Sellers
27. Joseph Stalin

28. The Atomic Weapons Research Establishment at Aldermaston
29. Christian Dior
30. Hungary

Quiz 10

Knowall's answer: "Fiery Fred" Trueman

1. Rudolf Nureyev
2. The *News of the World*
3. Vietnam
4. Prince Philip
5. Sophia Loren and Carlo Ponti
6. The Cultural Revolution
7. British PM Harold Macmillan
8. He burned himself to death
9. John Connally
10. Pope Paul and Archbishop of Canterbury Ramsey
11. Algeria
12. Walk in space
13. *Lady Chatterley's Lover*
14. Watts
15. "I'm backing Britain"
16. Ian Smith

17. Capital punishment
18. Biafra
19. The Kariba dam
20. Mods and Rockers
21. Graham Hill
22. South Africa
23. *Private Eye*
24. Foinavon (ridden by John Buckingham)
25. Paris
26. Mini-skirts
27. Sirhan Sirhan
28. Anthony Armstrong-Jones
29. 1968
30. Francis Chichester

Quiz 11

Knowall's answer: A Boeing 747 that carried it aloft

1. Afghanistan
2. Anwar Sadat
3. Dutch elm disease
4. John Cleese as Basil Fawlty
5. Managua, Nicaragua
6. Steve Biko
7. The Sex Pistols
8. 1 January 1973
9. Isabel Perón
10. "The Winter of Discontent"
11. Princess Anne
12. Skytrain
13. "Papa Doc" and "Baby Doc"
14. He was stabbed with a poisoned umbrella tip
15. SALT-2 (The Strategic Arms Limitation Treaty)
16. Himself and his visitors
17. Tony Jacklin

18. Lord Louis Mountbatten
19. Uganda
20. Bobby Fischer
21. Antonio Salazar
22. Bishop Abel Muzorewa
23. Flixborough
24. 1976
25. Charlie Chaplin
26. Pol Pot
27. Kent State (Ohio)
28. Sebastian Coe
29. J. Edgar Hoover
30. Red Rum

Quiz 12

Knowall's answer: Dan Quayle

1. John Lennon
2. Twentieth Century-Fox
3. Beijing's Tiananmen Square
4. Editor Ian Hislop (after Yorkshire Ripper's wife Sonia Sutcliffe was awarded £600,000)
5. Steffi Graf
6. Boris Yeltsin
7. Iran's
8. First American woman in space
9. Bicycle moto-cross
10. Libya
11. December 1988
12. The Tamil Tigers
13. Billy Butlin
14. The Penlee lifeboat
15. The Green Party
16. The America's Cup (yacht racing)
17. Live Aid (1985)
18. Armenia
19. Lech Walesa

20. The Palestine Liberation Organisation (PLO)
21. Benigno Aquino
22. Hillsborough, Sheffield
23. The Queen
24. The *Marchioness*
25. The "storm of the century" (16 October 1987)
26. Boycott the 1980 Olympic Games in Moscow
27. Bob Champion
28. PC Yvonne Fletcher
29. Dr Andrei Sakharov
30. At the Brandenburg Gate

Quiz 13

Knowall's answer: Rhodesia (Zimbabwe)
1. Clint Eastwood
2. Bjorn Borg
3. Beirut
4. The Delta Force
5. The San Francisco earthquake
6. Michael Foot
7. Enniskillen
8. Peter Sellers
9. Poland (Tadeusz Mazowiecki)
10. François Mitterand
11. Orgreave
12. He ordered the shooting down of an Iranian airliner
13. "The Guildford Four" (cleared in 1989 of IRA bombings after 14 years in prison)
14. Sir Anthony Meyer

15. The Golden Temple at Amritsar
16. The first crew coxed by a woman (Susan Brown)
17. Dublin
18. Geoffrey Boycott
19. An ambulance service
20. "The Gang of Four"
21. King Juan Carlos
22. Eric Morecambe
23. Robert Runcie
24. John Arlott
25. Mao Tse-tung's widow
26. Golf's Ryder Cup
27. South Georgia
28. David Steel
29. Townsend Thoresen
30. Laura Ashley

Quiz 14

Knowall's answer: Intelligence
1. John Major
2. Kobe
3. Australian Aboriginals
4. Jarvis Cocker
5. Export of live animals
6. Expo '92
7. Norway
8. Mike Gatting
9. 1991
10. Salman Rushdie
11. Ian Botham and Allan Lamb v Imran Khan
12. Heidi Fleiss
13. He won the "Grand National that never was" on Esha Ness (declared void after two false starts)
14. Fruitopia
15. Bill Clinton's
16. He was the first black Supreme Court judge
17. Betty Boothroyd
18. Tony Blair
19. The disc jockey
20. Plaid Cymru
21. A ship canal
22. The century-old carrier pigeon unit
23. Strangeways Prison
24. Nigel Short and Gary Kasparov
25. First woman pilot of Concorde
26. Windsor Castle
27. A comet
28. Chechnya
29. A glove
30. On the site of the Newbury by-pass

Quiz 15

Knowall's answer: A mechanical calculator
1. Barry Took
2. 37.1°C (98.8°F)
3. The 1993 car bombing of New York's World Trade Centre
4. Hoover
5. Austria, Finland and Sweden
6. Madrid
7. Clint Eastwood
8. F. W. de Klerk
9. NHS operations
10. The Soviet Union
11. Mars
12. Mikhail Gorbachev
13. Japan
14. Alison Hargreaves
15. Unfounded allegations of an extra-marital affair

16. Public relations
17. A series of nuclear tests
18. That of Oasis
19. Penguin Books
20. The White House, Moscow (parliament building)
21. Roman Catholic Bishop of Argyll and the Isles
22. Harrod's (Mohammed al-Fayed)
23. The ability to swim
24. Phoenix, Arizona
25. Disneyland Paris
26. Warrington
27. The White House, Washington D.C.
28. Michael Heseltine, Douglas Hurd and John Major
29. The world's press
30. *The Archers*

Quiz 16

Knowall's answer: Wayne Bobbit
1. Ultraheat treated
2. *Merry Xmas Everyone*
3. *Bugsy Malone*
4. A champion racehorse

ANSWERS

5. Dave Stewart
6. The Socialist Party
7. The Gaia theory
8. An explosive
9. Gordon Jackson
10. Bulgaria
11. A cruise missile
12. Princess Anne
13. *The Wizard of Oz*
14. Barbara Cartland
15. The Netherlands
16. On the Moon
17. Boot
18. Staffordshire
19. Murdering Gandhi
20. Sinead O'Connor
21. Nikita
22. The "speed" of film
23. Catalan
24. China
25. Mother Theresa
26. The Police
27. Rio de Janeiro
28. Nissan
29. One member, one vote
30. A boomerang

Quiz 17

**Knowall's answer:
William Masters and
Virginia Johnson**
1. Imran Khan
2. *Dancing in the Street*
3. Nigel
4. SS *France*
5. 12
6. ACAS (Advisory,
   Conciliation and
   Arbitration Service)
7. South Africa
8. They were all cars
   made by Triumph
9. The Attorney General

10. Barbie
11. Omar Sharif
12. The Finns
13. Cardinal Basil Hume
14. They are all Canadian
15. Faith, Hope and Charity
16. John Inverdale
17. Enoch Powell
18. *An Artist of the
    Floating World*
19. Five: USA, Russia,
    China, Britain, France
20. *Grand Hotel*
21. Munster
22. Jackie Onassis
    (Kennedy)
23. *Rainbow*
24. Ugandan president Idi
    Amin
25. Motown
26. Television transmission
27. Ballet
28. Indonesia
29. The *Stars and Stripes*
30. Anthony Fokker

Quiz 18

**Knowall's answer:
California**
1. *Sunset Boulevard*
2. Volgograd
3. The cello
4. The only words where
   the five vowels appear
   in the right order
5. British Airways
6. Niamh Kavanagh
7. Port Said
8. Wimbledon's No.1 Court
9. The UK
10. *Especially For You,
    Hand On Your Heart,
    Tears On My Pillow*

11. Barrister (lawyer)
12. India
13. Martha Longhurst
14. (Dame) Nellie Melba
15. The House of Lords
16. Micron (the others
    make up atoms)
17. James Last
18. *Swallows and Amazons*
19. Bass
20. *The Streets of San
    Francisco*
21. Keith Joseph
22. November 1994
23. Portugal
24. *A Passage to India*
25. King George V's silver
    jubilee
26. A circle
27. Gertrude Lawrence
28. Pocahontas
29. 1986
30. Lord Carrington

Quiz 19

**Knowall's answer:
Magenta**
1. *Star Wars*
2. Green

3. Cormorant
4. Duke
5. 20.2°C
6. IND
7. Ruby
8. The
9. The brazil
10. 43
11. 2 November
12. Lace
13. 6.45am
14. Saffron
15. Nitrogen (78.08%)
16. *Country Life*
17. 46
18. Oxford
19. 28 bore
20. Girl Guides
21. 640
22. Mars
23. Red
24. India
25. Ceylon (1960–65;
    Mrs Bandaranaike)
26. 20
27. Hayward
28. 1967
29. Ian McEwan
30. 47

Quiz 20

**Knowall's answer: He was
poisoned with arsenic-
laced chocolates**
1. Nick Leeson's
2. John and Bobby
   Kennedy
3. That of Prince Charles
   and Princess Diana
4. Sarah Bernhardt
5. Edwina Currie
6. Captain Mark Phillips
7. *The Ed Sullivan Show*

8. Salvador Allende's Chilean government
9. Richard Nixon
10. Christiaan Barnard
11. Rudyard Kipling
12. Buddy Holly
13. Lillie Langtry
14. Yuri Andropov
15. France
16. Ben Johnson
17. Tony Hancock
18. Lockheed
19. Joy Adamson
20. D. H. Lawrence's (*Women in Love*)
21. Pierre Laval
22. Lee Marvin
23. The Piltdown Man
24. Adolf Eichmann
25. General Dwight Eisenhower
26. Jane Fonda
27. Yasser Arafat
28. My Lai
29. Arthur Ashe
30. Guy Burgess, Donald Maclean, Kim Philby

Quiz 21

Knowall's answer: Michael Heseltine
1. Al Capone
2. Dr Marie Stopes (The Mothers' Clinic)
3. Allen Ginsberg
4. President Warren Harding
5. Marlon Brando's son (Christian)
6. "Squidgy"
7. Brendan Behan
8. Sir Arthur "Bomber" Harris

9. Greta Garbo
10. Chappaquiddick Island
11. The Unknown Soldier's
12. Aldo Moro
13. Germaine Greer
14. Lord Carnarvon
15. The Bank of Credit and Commerce International (BCCI)
16. Menachem Begin's
17. John Profumo
18. Charlie Chaplin's
19. Che Guevara
20. Mae West
21. Hermann Goering
22. Major Richard Bong
23. Whitewater
24. Louis Mountbatten, later Lord
25. Judy Garland
26. Pablo Escobar
27. Truman Capote
28. Steffi Graf's
29. Lavrenti Beria
30. Lord Moynihan

Quiz 22

Knowall's answer: Alger Hiss
1. He was the last man to be executed in the UK
2. Eduard Shevardnadze
3. Anglia Television
4. Fidel Castro's
5. The *Washington Post*
6. Manuel Noriega
7. Clean-up campaigner Mary Whitehouse
8. *Oh! Calcutta!*
9. Billie Holliday
10. Spiro T. Agnew
11. King Farouk
12. Frankie Howerd and

Benny Hill
13. William Randolph Hearst
14. Lord Lambton
15. "Lady" Rose Aberdour
16. Pamella Bordes
17. Captain of the *Titanic* (lost with the ship)
18. Glenn Miller
19. Benazir Bhutto
20. Cork
21. John Stonehouse
22. Boris Pasternak
23. Horatio Bottomley
24. "The Butcher of Lyons"
25. Jim Bakker
26. Noddy
27. Dr Klaus Fuchs
28. Huey "Kingfish" Long
29. Anne Frank's
30. Marion Barry

Quiz 23

Knowall's answer: Linda Eastman
1. Brigitte Bardot
2. David Mellor
3. Wallis Simpson
4. Joan Collins
5. Judy Garland
6. Richard Gere

7. The Duchess of York (Fergie)
8. Warren Beatty
9. Kenneth Branagh
10. Andre Agassi
11. Katharine Hepburn
12. D. H. Lawrence
13. Jack Nicholson
14. Cher
15. Bill Clinton
16. Group Captain Peter Townsend
17. Lauren Bacall
18. Sarah Keays
19. Marilyn Monroe
20. John Lloyd
21. Frank Sinatra and André Previn
22. Viscount Althorp (Earl Spencer)
23. Desi Arnaz
24. Elizabeth Taylor
25. Lady Bienvenida Buck
26. Grace Kelly
27. Demi Moore
28. Sophia Loren
29. Timothy Dalton
30. Douglas Fairbanks (Snr)

Quiz 24

Knowall's answer: The Financial Times 100 Share Index
1. The Beatles
2. Margaret Thatcher
3. The BBC
4. Jack Nicklaus
5. Richard Nixon
6. Laurence Olivier
7. Gracie Fields
8. Harold Macmillan
9. Jimmy White
10. Ian Botham

ANSWERS

11. William Cody
12. Bruce Springsteen
13. James Hunt
14. Frank Sinatra
15. The Queen
16. John Wayne
17. Al Capone
18. Mick Jagger
19. Elle Macpherson
20. Ronnie Barker and
    Ronnie Corbett
21. Brigitte Bardot
22. Lynn Davies
23. Ian St John
24. William Joyce
25. Desert Orchid
26. Noël Coward
27. John McEnroe
28. Bill Clinton
29. Benny Goodman
30. Nat Lofthouse

Quiz 25

Knowall's answer: A shire horse
1. Hosts Uruguay
2. USA
3. Harold Wilson
4. Max Schmeling
5. Confused usage of
   English
6. Germany (European
   Championship)
7. Fred Housego
8. *Palme d'Or* for best
   film
9. Harold Abrahams
10. Dennis Conner
11. Freshwater angling
12. Eric Bristow
13. Peter Collins
14. William Golding
15. 1976-77 and 1977-78

16. Campaign for Real Ale
    (CAMRA)
17. *Citizen Kane*
18. Roald Dahl
19. Richard Ingrams
20. Most Valuable Player
21. Aberdeen (1984-85)
22. Miss America
23. World bowls
24. Gary Kasparov
25. English Wine of the Year
26. Lancashire
27. Toy of the Year
28. Crossword puzzle
    solving
29. Chester Barnes
30. Robbie Coltrane for
    Cracker

Quiz 26

**Knowall's answer:
Agatha Christie**
1. Ffyona Campbell
2. A record ocean descent
   of 10,916 metres
   (35,814ft)
3. Pass her driving test
4. He dribbled a basketball
5. In the orbiting space
   station MIR

6. By breathing with scuba
   equipment
7. A Toyota Landcruiser
8. A paper aeroplane
9. Don Allum
10. Restaurant meals (as a
    grader)
11. Reinhold Messner
12. A solo transatlantic
    crossing
13. By hitting a slot-
    machine jackpot
14. The Mississippi
15. Donovan Bailey
16. Flew an inverted
    aeroplane
17. A motorbike
18. A ping-pong ball
19. Placido Domingo
20. Reached the summit of
    Everest without oxygen
21. Per Lindstrand and
    Richard Branson
22. A boomerang
23. On a life-raft at sea
24. A unicycle
25. Sir Ranulph Fiennes
    and Mike Stroud
26. 41 points
27. Flown solo around the
    world
28. A Volkswagen Beetle
29. The Sears Tower,
    Chicago
30. Sail non-stop
    (unsupported)
    around the world

Quiz 27

**Knowall's answer:
David Lean**
1. Dr Timothy Leary
2. Harold Macmillan

3. Oliver Hardy to Stan
   Laurel
4. Charles de Gaulle
5. Henry Ford, talking
   about the Model 'T',
   the world's first
   mass-produced car
6. Salman Rushdie,
   following the
   publication of
   The Satanic Verses
7. Theodore (Teddy)
   Roosevelt
8. Winston Churchill
9. Groucho Marx, on
   resigning from a
   Beverly Hills club
10. Edward (Earl) Grey;
    "we shall not see them
    lit again in our lifetime"
    is the full quotation
11. Sam Goldwyn
12. British prime minister
    Neville Chamberlain
13. Rhett Butler (Clark
    Gable) to Scarlett
    O'Hara (Vivien Leigh)
    in *Gone with the Wind*
14. Emperor Franz Josef of
    Austria-Hungary
15. Andy Warhol
16. Mao Tse-tung
17. Los Angeles
18. Mae West
19. Harold Wilson
20. James Cagney, though
    the nearest he actually
    came was "You dirty
    double-crossing rat" in
    Blonde Crazy (1931)
21. Dorothy Parker
22. British PM David Lloyd
    George

23. Eldridge Cleaver
24. Noël Coward
25. John F. Kennedy
26. Orson Welles
27. Neil Armstrong after landing on the moon in 1969
28. Orphan (Italian foreign minister Count Ciano in 1942)
29. Franklin D. Roosevelt
30. W. C. Fields

Quiz 28

Knowall's answer:
Politically correct
1. A QUasi-Autonomous Non-Governmental Organisation
2. The homeless
3. A ghetto-blaster
4. The crowd in a sports arena
5. Being shot at by your own side in war
6. A white adult male suspect
7. Bureau of State Security (South Africa)
8. Eat at a McDonald's fast-food restaurant
9. Mutually Assured (nuclear) Destruction
10. A dustman
11. Old people
12. Referee's assistants
13. Words a minute
14. During World War 2 ("Kilroy was here" became a widely used graffiti slogan)
15. The "good" cop and the "bad" cop
16. Intervening positively on behalf of minority groups or individuals
17. Cocaine
18. Spin-doctors
19. A prisoner (it is a cell)
20. President Reagan's free market economics
21. It is a vehicle wheel clamp
22. Cat (in the NATO voice alphabet)
23. Television broadcasting satellites
24. An Impact Disguised Suicide (in a car crash)
25. To score fast at the beginning of a limited overs match
26. Someone who needs false teeth
27. Local development ("Not In My Back Yard")
28. "Good luck"
29. A young upwardly mobile professional
30. Zone Improvement Plan code

Quiz 29

Knowall's answer:
The Joker
1. The Fantastic Four
2. Adam West and Burt Ward
3. Captain America
4. Jimmy Olsen
5. Dr Bruce Banner, physicist
6. Mandrake
7. Scout
8. Iceman and Fire-Star
9. Wonder Woman
10. Mega-City One
11. Michelangelo, Leonardo, Donatello and Raphael
12. Mighty Mouse
13. The Phantom
14. Popeye and Bluto
15. The Mask
16. The Shadow
17. The Silver Surfer
18. They are cousins
19. Mother Nature, Spotty
20. Grey
21. Johnny Weissmuller
22. Thor
23. Wolverine
24. El Zorro (the fox)
25. The Champions
26. Barbara Gordon, Commissioner Gordon
27. Lex Luthor
28. 1939
29. Michael Crawford
30. He is a freelance photo-journalist

Quiz 30

Knowall's answer: Björk
1. The "black and tans"
2. Tesco (overtaking

Sainsbury)
3. Missouri
4. Pierre Cardin
5. The gums
6. Malawi
7. Croquet
8. *Coronation Street*
9. Willy Russell
10. Charlie Kray
11. Ross Perot
12. Jimi Hendrix
13. Viscount Stansgate
14. Green, white and orange
15. £2 million
16. *Jessica*
17. The Shah of Iran, in exile in the USA
18. Salem, Massachusetts
19. Mud
20. Rhino horns
21. India
22. Theology
23. Britt Ekland (the only one not to have married John Derek)
24. Formosa
25. Lou Costello
26. British ambassador to Dublin
27. *The Player*
28. Biggles
29. Gordon Kaye
30. Dusty Springfield

Quiz 31

Knowall's answer:
A Chorus Line
1. Donovan
2. 42
3. Romania
4. *Step It Up, Ground Level, Creation*

ANSWERS

5. Indira Gandhi in India (15 years in two periods of office)
6. A bill
7. Indonesia
8. The IMF (International Monetary Fund)
9. Norman Painting
10. Charles de Gaulle
11. William
12. London
13. William Douglas-Home
14. Stonehenge
15. Geoffrey Howe
16. "Evening all"
17. Cadillac
18. 1996
19. Trevor Francis
20. Rob Collins
21. Dennis Skinner
22. Stanley Baldwin
23. French horn, trombone, trumpet, tuba
24. Michael Portillo: he appeared in a TV ad for the product when aged eight
25. It was stolen and killed in Ireland
26. Bonzo Dog Doo-Dah Band
27. The Duke of Windsor
28. 1950
29. Doug Mountjoy
30. The BBC

Quiz 32

Knowall's answer: Cliff Richard (*Mistletoe and Wine*)
1. Jimmy Carter
2. *To Kill A Mockingbird*
3. James Whitaker

4. The perigee
5. Kamikaze
6. Cheltenham
7. Broadway
8. Peter Davison
9. *The Piano*
10. Chris Sutton
11. A mirage
12. Tossing the caber
13. 1924
14. Denim
15. PEN
16. Minolta (the 7000)
17. Oscar Wilde's
18. Alan Jay Lerner
19. The ozone layer
20. The USSR
21. Sir Malcolm Sargent
22. Bosnia
23. They became the first Britons to climb Everest
24. St Petersburg
25. David Niven
26. Pakistan
27. Crystal Palace: The FA Cup final (Spurs v Sheffield United 2-2)
28. Cassandra
29. The Gold Coast
30. Denmark and the Republic of Ireland

Quiz 33

Knowall's answer: The Walkman
1. The atomic bomb
2. Diodes
3. The automatic pilot
4. Carbon dioxide
5. The pop-up toaster
6. The atom
7. AEG

8. He invented the aerosol
9. Jodrell Bank, Cheshire
10. His face was the first television image
11. "Puffing Billy"
12. The "iron lung"
13. "Star Wars"
14. Guglielmo Marconi
15. It was nuclear powered
16. The electric guitar
17. He deployed chlorine gas to harm and the gas mask to protect
18. The relaying of communications by satellite
19. Hans Geiger
20. The hovercraft
21. Queen Alexandra
22. Freon
23. 320 km (200 miles)
24. IBM
25. Radar
26. 1907 (by Arthur Korn)
27. The tape recorder
28. A viable colour television system
29. He invented the ejector seat
30. The 1930s (1937)

Quiz 34

Knowall's answer: The loudspeaker
1. The heart
2. Enrico Fermi (1942)
3. The computer
4. Rolex
5. Silicon
6. The first liquid fuel rocket
7. He invented the parking meter

8. The anode
9. Films
10. The transistor
11. Binary digit
12. The microwave oven
13. Meltdown
14. He formulated sun-tan cream
15. New York
16. Diesel-Engined Road Vehicle
17. The compact disc
18. The starter motor for cars
19. An atomic clock
20. High Definition Television
21. A particle accelerator
22. Satellites in space
23. Charles Goodyear
24. The non-stick pan
25. In the world's first helicopter (1907)
26. Carbon fibre
27. The decompression chamber
28. Germany (1910)
29. Invention of the lawn-mower (1902)

30. A shave (he invented the electric razor in 1928)

Quiz 35

Knowall's answer: The World Trade Centre, New York

1. Switzerland
2. The Thames Barrier
3. The TransAlaska Pipeline System
4. "Spaghetti Junction"
5. The George Washington Bridge
6. The Canada Tower, Canary Wharf
7. First meeting of English and French Channel Tunnel construction teams
8. The Barbican
9. *Biosphere 2*
10. Sewage
11. The Hubble Space Telescope
12. Rollercoaster
13. The Jubilee Line
14. The Aswan High Dam
15. The Liverpool-Birkenhead Mersey Tunnel
16. The SkyDome, Toronto
17. Japan (Honshu and Hokkaido)
18. The Severn
19. Spain
20. A deep-water jetty
21. Viking 1 and Viking 2
22. The Pan-American Highway
23. The Empire State Building
24. The Maracaña

municipal stadium
25. Poland
26. The Humber Bridge
27. A new industrial city
28. San Antonio
29. Sizewell B
30. The Golden Gate Bridge

Quiz 36

Knowall's answer: Ford

1. Lamborghini
2. Moving space shuttles
3. The Silver Shadow I
4. "Big Ben", the world's biggest motorcycle
5. *Duel* (1971)
6. A 1962 Ferrari 250
7. Fastest steam-powered car
8. The MacLaren F1
9. A dumper truck
10. 5.7 seconds (633.468mph)
11. The *Graf Zeppelin*
12. *Half-Safe* was amphibious
13. The experimental aircraft *Voyager*
14. BMW
15. The *Blackbird*

16. A Lancia
17. By a rocket engine
18. As the home of Lotus
19. Zil limousines
20. The Jaguar XJ220 (conceived at the height of 1980s car mania but over-priced by the time deliveries began)
21. The B-2
22. Grand tourer
23. Paul Stewart (son of Jackie)
24. It is the fastest fire-engine ever
25. Leyland
26. The Royale
27. Harley-Davidson and Indian
28. MG (MGF, 1995)
29. A powerboat crossing of the Atlantic
30. Ferrari

Quiz 37

Knowall's answer: Buying a round of drinks (to discourage wartime workers from drinking)

1. They were cousins
2. Great Yarmouth and King's Lynn
3. Jutland
4. 65 miles (105km)
5. Theodore "Teddy" Roosevelt
6. Gallipoli in the Dardanelles
7. British Summer Time
8. The USA's
9. Sir Douglas Haig
10. The first parachute descent from a

powered aircraft
11. Jerusalem
12. 1914
13. The Cameroons
14. 14
15. The Central Powers
16. The Sopwith Camel
17. Spanish flu
18. Austria's
19. Field Marshal Paul von Hindenburg
20. September
21. A fast sub-chasing boat
22. The River Marne
23. Windsor and Mountbatten (the royal family changed their names)
24. The USA
25. The Royal Flying Corps
26. 1,069
27. Ekaterinburg
28. General "Black Jack" Pershing
29. 2 million
30. The Siegfried Line

Quiz 38

Knowall's answer: Their servants

1. Belgian neutrality
2. Military conscription
3. Skyros
4. The tank
5. Alexander Kerensky
6. Mons
7. 45 miles (72km)
8. Brest-Litovsk
9. King George V
10. 17 June
11. Mata Hari
12. The Falkland Islands
13. Lenin

ANSWERS

14. The War Cabinet
15. Turkey
16. David Lloyd George
17. Scarborough, Whitby, Hartlepool and West Hartlepool
18. Captain T. E. Lawrence (Lawrence of Arabia)
19. Marshal Ferdinand Foch
20. British ships flew American flags
21. The Red Baron
22. 1 million
23. Chlorine gas
24. Holland
25. Lord Kitchener
26. The convoy system
27. "Peace attack"
28. The Somme
29. The 11th hour of the 11th day of the 11th month (11 November 1918)
30. The Treaty of Versailles

Quiz 39

Knowall's answer: Winston Churchill
1. 3 September
2. Tankgrad, beyond the Urals
3. The Supermarine Spitfire and Hawker Hurricane
4. 6 June (D-Day – the Allied invasion of France)
5. Monte Cassino
6. The *Royal Oak*
7. 47
8. Singapore
9. General Douglas MacArthur

10. The Afrika Korps
11. Remagen
12. 56
13. Grand Admiral Karl Doenitz
14. The Russo-Finnish Winter War
15. Toulon
16. The A-4
17. Kursk
18. Rheims (in a school house)
19. 55 million
20. Germany *and* Russia
21. Okinawa
22. El Alamein
23. General Dwight D. Eisenhower
24. Leon Trotsky
25. They breached the Ruhr's Mohne and Eder dams
26. The Home Guard ("Dad's Army")
27. First US ship torpedoed by a U-boat (before America entered the war)
28. Messerschmitt 262
29. Breda and Enfield (the Bren gun)
30. It took place in the railway coach used for Germany's surrender in 1918

Quiz 40

Knowall's answer: Vienna
1. The Dunkirk evacuation (1940)
2. Dieppe
3. The engine stopped

4. The *Volksturm* (People's Guard)
5. The Channel Islands
6. Italy
7. Warsaw
8. Sword
9. The Oxfam famine aid charity
10. It was awarded to an island – the people of Malta
11. General George Patton
12. Peenemunde Island
13. An Arctic convoy to Murmansk
14. The mass grave of 4,000 Polish officers shot by the Russians
15. Arnhem
16. Lord Haw-Haw (William Joyce)
17. The USA's
18. His mistress
19. The T-34
20. Mining
21. P. G. Wodehouse
22. Stalingrad
23. The majority of the dead were Italian POWs
24. Russia
25. "Werewolves"
26. 1942
27. The *Ark Royal*

28. The Duke of Kent (George VI's younger brother)
29. The Comintern
30. Iwo Jima

Quiz 41

Knowall's answer: France
1. The Scud
2. North Korea
3. Field Marshal Lord Roberts
4. President Nasser's seizure of the Suez Canal
5. India and Pakistan
6. Rex Hunt
7. Yugoslavia
8. 192
9. Inchon
10. Jomo "Burning Spear" Kenyatta
11. The Six-Day War (Israel versus the Arabs, 1967)
12. Three (shot by Royal Marines defending Government House)
13. Nicaragua
14. Russia's
15. President Johnson
16. Afghanistan
17. "Operation Desert Storm"
18. Turkey
19. South Georgia
20. China and Vietnam
21. The Exocet
22. The Tet (New Year) Offensive
23. The Cold War
24. Dubrovnik
25. Colonel "H" Jones
26. Japan

ANSWERS

27. At the 38th paralllel
28. 100 hours
29. 1975
30. Dayton, Ohio (The Dayton Accord)

Quiz 42

Knowall's answer: Daniel arap Moi
1. Robben Island
2. Pakistan
3. The Nazis
4. Rev. Ian Paisley
5. Tehran (Iran) and Yalta (the Crimea, Russia)
6. Jacques Chirac, mayor of the French capital, after his election as president
7. Indonesia
8. Leonid Brezhnev (Soviet Union) and Richard Nixon (USA)
9. The (Belgian) Congo
10. Dame Shirley Porter
11. 1922
12. Slovenia and Croatia
13. The Zulus
14. All were assassinated (1975, 1981, 1996)
15. Canada
16. Boutros Boutros Ghali (UN Secretaries-General since 1945)
17. Alan Bond
18. *Pravda*
19. Alexander Dubcek
20. Juan Perón
21. Iceland
22. 1956
23. Barry Goldwater
24. Tonga
25. Iran and Iraq

26. Russia
27. Charles Haughey
28. Greece, over the Turkish invasion of Cyprus
29. Carl Bildt
30. Switzerland

Quiz 43

Knowall's answer: Fidel Castro
1. New York
2. France
3. Jawaharlal Nehru, India's first PM from 1947 to 1964 (Indira was not related to "Mahatma" Gandhi)
4. Setting fire to the Reichstag, the German parliament building
5. Archbishop Makarios of Cyprus
6. South Africa
7. Tsar Nicholas II
8. Vienna
9. Gandhi
10. Peru
11. Kwame Nkrumah (1957-66)
12. The Mujaheddin ("holy warriors")
13. Egypt
14. Colin Powell
15. Nicolae Ceauçescu
16. Imelda Marcos
17. Robert Menzies
18. Violence at two World Cup qualifying matches; it was called "The Soccer War"
19. The Basques of northern Spain

20. Croatia
21. Haiti
22. Czechoslovakia
23. Menachem Begin
24. The Geneva Convention
25. Saddam Hussein
26. André Malraux, 10 years as minister for culture
27. New Zealand
28. China
29. George V, on the pact between Sir Samuel Hoare and Pierre Laval over Abyssinia, 1935
30. Paul Keating

Quiz 44

Knowall's answer: John Curry
1. Blackpool's
2. A moped
3. Golda Meir
4. *Sailor Beware*
5. In Northern Italy
6. A lie-detector test
7. Australia v West Indies (who won by 17 runs)
8. Harpo

9. The "Yom Kippur War"
10. Rock and mountain climbing
11. What You See Is What You Get
12. 1959
13. Sharpeville
14. Roald Dahl
15. Princess Grace of Monaco
16. Radio Caroline
17. Captain
18. 2 weeks
19. Luxembourg and Strasbourg
20. Zola Budd
21. 1977
22. Steve McQueen
23. 1916
24. Pope John Paul I
25. Charlie Chan
26. A "bear"
27. 1976
28. King's Cross
29. "TW3"
30. Corazon Aquino

Quiz 45

Knowall's answer: She drowned (possibly suicide)
1. Bill Shankly
2. John
3. They're both Canary Islands
4. Benito Mussolini
5. The Campaign for Nuclear Disarmament
6. George Harrison
7. Oscar (the others are film titles)
8. The Tay
9. Johan Cruyff
10. The liver

ANSWERS

11. Jack Hobbs
12. Apartheid
13. *Cut-throat Island*
14. The St Leger at Doncaster
15. Helmut Kohl
16. Seven
17. Lassa fever
18. Optical Character Recognition
19. The Referendum Party
20. A crocodile
21. Scott Joplin
22. Food additives
23. The election of a new pope
24. Transcendental meditation
25. Ronan Point
26. Equity
27. *Lucky Jim* by Kingsley Amis
28. G7 (The group of seven)
29. George Burns
30. Malawi

Quiz 46

Knowall's answer: Australia
1. World's 10 highest waterfalls
2. An insect
3. Fungi
4. 1946
5. Michael Caine
6. Krypton
7. Sikhism
8. They can all be pink
9. Royal National Lifeboat Institution
10. A minute
11. The cabbage
12. The ant

13. Harry Houdini
14. The trombone
15. Ronald Reagan
16. Ligament
17. Richard Adams
18. A bird
19. Bahrain
20. The Netherlands and Belgium
21. Mick
22. Eight
23. William Whitelaw
24. Albania
25. Mali
26. The Hague (Netherlands)
27. Egypt
28. Jean Sibelius
29. John Howard
30. Three

Quiz 47

Knowall's answer: Crop circles
1. The Himalayas
2. Vampires
3. The Loch Ness monster
4. He made the first "official" UFO sighting
5. The giant squid
6. Inexplicable lights
7. Lewis Carroll (Charles Dodgson)
8. Giant monitor lizards
9. The US Air Force, to investigate UFO sightings
10. Rowing solo across the Atlantic
11. Pluckley, Kent
12. Bigfoot
13. The sinking of the *Titanic*

14. Chasing a UFO
15. Agatha Christie
16. "Noisy spirit"
17. They are all "haunted"
18. Exposing fake "spirits"
19. Through a ouija board
20. The Magic Circle
21. The runes
22. Uri Geller
23. The Bermuda Triangle
24. Extra-Terrestrial Intelligence
25. Voodoo
26. Divining or dowsing
27. Ley lines
28. In "The Beyond" or on "The Other Side"
29. The Kelly-Hopkinsville Goblin
30. Anastasia

Quiz 48

Knowall's answer: Monica Seles
1. The Camorra
2. Ronnie Kray
3. Broadwater Farm
4. "Scarface" Al Capone
5. Ronald Biggs
6. Clive Ponting

7. Brinks-Mat's (in 1983)
8. Ian Brady and Myra Hindley
9. Ronald Reagan
10. Sir Roger Casement
11. Fred and Rosemary West
12. Princess Anne
13. Kenya
14. O. J. Simpson
15. Albany, Camp Hill, Parkhurst
16. McDonalds
17. Beverly Allitt
18. Howard Hughes
19. Roberto Calvi
20. Dennis Nilsen
21. John Christie (guilty) and Timothy Evans (innocent)
22. Ruth Ellis (1953)
23. Darius Guppy
24. As "The Boston Strangler"
25. James Hanratty
26. The Manson Family
27. Derek Bentley
28. Patty Hearst
29. Dr Hawley Harvey Crippen
30. Olaf Palme

Quiz 49

Knowall's answer: George Raft
1. The Golden Triangle
2. "The Yorkshire Ripper"
3. The "cat burglar"
4. The US Treasury
5. Judge Giovanni Falcone
6. James Bulger
7. Gary Gilmour
8. Billy Hill and Jack Spot

ANSWERS

9. Bonnie Parker and Clyde Barrow
10. Carlo Gambino
11. Mary Flora Bell
12. Blackmailing manufacturers or stores by threatening to contaminate products
13. The Chicago White Sox
14. Peter (Perac) Rachman
15. Hand-guns
16. Knightsbridge
17. Kenneth Noye
18. Michael Ryan
19. The now-failed Bank of Credit and Commerce International (BCCI)
20. They were the unfortunate train driver and fireman in the Great Train Robbery (1963)
21. Jacques Mesrine
22. Machine-gun Kelly
23. Medellín and Cali
24. The Richardsons
25. 1924
26. "Murder Incorporated"
27. John De Lorean
28. "The Untouchables"
29. Charles "Lucky" Luciano
30. Michael Milken

Quiz 50

Knowall's answer: Chelsea
1. Bruce Springsteen
2. Stokely Carmichael
3. Ciccone
4. *The Shootist*
5. David
6. Polio
7. Mickey Mouse

8. "The Birdman of Alcatraz"
9. Larry Hagman ("JR" in *Dallas)*
10. General Colin Powell
11. *From Here to Eternity*
12. Snoopy
13. Donald Duck
14. His (stillborn) twin brother
15. Microsoft
16. Jack Lemmon and Walter Matthau
17. Thomas Dewey
18. Rodney King
19. Jimmy Carter
20. *Monopoly*
21. Joseph Heller
22. Robert Redford
23. Woodrow Wilson (taking the US into World War 1 in 1917)
24. Eugene O'Neill
25. Robert Altman
26. Leonard Bernstein
27. First woman Supreme Court judge (1981)
28. Tom and Jerry
29. Nat King Cole
30. To be canonised as a saint

Quiz 51

Knowall's answer: Noël Coward
1. *Come Dancing* (1950)
2. Longleat
3. Alan Bennett, Peter Cook, Jonathan Miller, Dudley Moore
4. Prince Charles
5. Clydebank, Glasgow
6. Reg Smythe

7. Ski-jumping; he came last
8. The Ford Escort
9. Sir Frederick Ashton
10. Bud Flanagan
11. Harold Wilson (1965)
12. Sir Edward Elgar
13. Peter Ustinov
14. Gloster Meteor (1944)
15. Cliff Richard
16. Emily Davison
17. Skytrain
18. Bradford
19. Barnes Wallis
20. Peter Sellers
21. The Home Guard
22. *The Romans in Britain*
23. A black felt hat
24. Christopher Fry
25. The Phantom
26. On a postage stamp
27. Janice Nicholls
28. John (Lord) Reith
29. Group Captain Leonard Cheshire, V.C.
30. Modesty Blaise

Quiz 52

Knowall's answer: St George
1. British Gas
2. J. M. Barrie
3. "Tiny" Rowland
4. First Lord of the Admiralty
5. Glenda Jackson
6. Aneurin Bevan
7. David Lloyd George
8. Prince Andrew of Greece and Princess Alice, grand-daughter of Queen Victoria
9. John Betjeman

10. Lord Jesse Boot
11. C. B. Fry
12. The *Victoria & Albert*
13. Robert Bolt
14. Viscount Montgomery of Alamein
15. Wandsworth and Westminster
16. Hugh Dowding
17. Edward Morgan
18. 1945
19. The famous "policeman on a white horse" who cleared the pitch after fans invaded it
20. Alfred Hitchcock
21. It was the first Cabinet post given to a woman
22. Albert Finney
23. Stanley Baldwin
24. Jim Clark
25. Bill Brandt
26. Gustav Holst
27. Kevin Maxwell
28. Gertrude Jekyll
29. Adrian Boult
30. Baron Austin

Quiz 53

Knowall's answer: The lemming
1. Lichens
2. Vivian Fuchs

ANSWERS

3. Greenland
4. First to fly over the South Pole
5. Mt Erebus
6. Scott's wife Kathleen
7. Admiral Robert Peary (USA)
8. Sea-lions
9. The Beaufort Scale for measuring wind speed
10. Europe
11. Roald Amundsen
12. 90%
13. *Ice Station Zebra*
14. The *Endurance*
15. Blue fox
16. Vinson Massif
17. Looking after the ponies
18. Scott plus Bowers, Evans, Oates and Wilson
19. 55 metres
20. Dr Frederick Cook
21. British Antarctic Territory
22. Umberto Nobile
23. The USA's
24. Ranulph Fiennes
25. It was undertaken by

submarine (The *Nautilus*)
26. Baffin Island
27. 42 miles (68km)
28. Captain Ernest Shackleton
29. Bull and cow
30. 12

Quiz 54

Knowall's answer: The *Braer*
1. 1971
2. Blue
3. Bhopal
4. Thermal Oxide
5. Pesticides
6. Ukraine
7. CFCs (chlorofluorocarbons)
8. "Slash and burn"
9. London (Athens came bottom of the 23-city survey)
10. Brazil, Denmark, Iceland, Japan, Norway, Peru, Russia, South Korea
11. The Rhine
12. Rio de Janeiro
13. World Wildlife Fund (WWF)
14. The beluga whale
15. Council for the Protection of Rural England
16. Bangladesh
17. Antarctica
18. Cornwall
19. The Great Barrier Reef off Australia
20. British
21. Ralph Nader

22. The avocet
23. Carbon dioxide
24. The Sahel
25. The *Rainbow Warrior*
26. Sulphur dioxide (SO_3)
27. The Netherlands
28. Smog (SMoke and fOG)
29. Three Mile Island
30. Methane

Quiz 55

Knowall's answer: Cartography
1. Aries
2. Latin and Italian
3. Quartz
4. Hallowe'en
5. New Mexico, Texas
6. Florence
7. The decibel
8. An edible leaf
9. Jarvis Cocker
10. Czech
11. Sodium
12. 20
13. A fletcher
14. The M62
15. George Bush
16. The dog licence
17. Japan
18. The paladin
19. Tom Stoppard
20. Le Mans
21. The Knights of the Garter
22. The Edinburgh Festival
23. On hind legs
24. The US dollar
25. Shrove Tuesday
26. 5-star General
27. Denmark
28. Muhammad Ali

29. Hillman
30. John Smith

Quiz 56

Knowall's answer: Evonne Goolagong
1. Tromsø
2. Militant Tendency
3. The Shah of Iran
4. Wendy
5. Tennis (the others use bats)
6. Stigmata
7. Ronald Searle
8. Sadler's Wells
9. Senator George Mitchell
10. Jaguar (owned by Ford)
11. The Shadows
12. Huddersfield
13. Anthea Turner
14. Ibrox Park, Glasgow
15. Pennsylvania and Maryland
16. The Ho Chi Minh Trail
17. Green (the others are the primaries used in 4-colour printing)
18. Swiss
19. Tony Lock
20. The A-Team (the others all involved distinctive transformations)
21. Giacomo Agostini
22. Peruvian
23. Beefeaters
24. Douglas Bader
25. The Royal Albert Hall
26. Linford Christie
27. Albert Camus
28. Airey Neave
29. Glyndebourne
30. Great Britain

ANSWERS

Quiz 57

Knowall's answer:
The (US) Virgin Islands
1. The human
2. A farthing
3. Lives
4. The Sears Tower
5. Truro
6. Hard black
7. The cruzeiro
8. Seaweed
9. Bruce Forsyth
10. Guernsey
11. Mercury
12. Artichoke
13. Chris Patten
14. Iceland
15. Earl
16. Polo
17. The Norwegian government
18. 28
19. A dime
20. Types of spaniel
21. Algeria and Libya
22. A hemisphere
23. November
24. The three terms at Oxford University
25. 22
26. Aluminium
27. The mink (otters are now protected)
28. China (14)
29. 30
30. Edinburgh

Quiz 58

Knowall's answer:
Tennessee Williams
1. *Cider with Rosie*
2. *Animal Farm*
3. *The Colour Purple*
4. Philosophy
5. *Justine*
6. Paul Gaugin's
7. Siegfried Sassoon and Wilfred Owen
8. Manderley
9. Truman Capote
10. Joanna Trollope
11. Frederick Forsyth
12. Africa
13. Harold Pinter
14. Adrian Mole
15. Alan Hollinghurst
16. The Larkins
17. William Brown
18. Compton Mackenzie
19. Lake Wobegon
20. Virginia Woolf
21. *Schindler's Ark* by Thomas Keneally
22. Kingsley and Martin Amis
23. Slough
24. The dalmatian (*101 Dalmatians*)
25. Dennis Potter
26. Jeeves
27. Teacher
28. *The Tale of Peter Rabbit*
29. Clare Francis
30. Richard Hannay

Quiz 59

Knowall's answer:
Fay Weldon
1. Edith Nesbit
2. *Beloved*
3. The Spanish Civil War
4. *The Horse Whisperer*
5. Arthur Ransome
6. J. D. Salinger
7. *The Call of the Wild*
8. Berlin
9. George Bernard Shaw
10. *On the Road*
11. The Fens
12. Julian Barnes
13. W. B. Yeats
14. Robertson Davies
15. Elizabeth Jane Howard
16. The Starkadders
17. G. K. Chesterton
18. *The Stone Diaries*
19. Colleen McCullough
20. Charles Ryder
21. *Loot*
22. *Tarka the Otter*
23. Thomas Mann's
24. Bathsheba (Everdene)
25. New York
26. Iris Murdoch
27. John Masefield
28. *The Buddha of Suburbia*
29. Erskine Childers
30. Antonia Fraser

Quiz 60

Knowall's answer:
W. Somerset Maugham
1. Alan Bennett
2. *The Remains of the Day*
3. *A Suitable Boy*
4. A. E. Housman
5. Sylvia Plath
6. Mrs Morel
7. *Lord of the Flies* by William Golding
8. *Lolita*
9. Margaret and Helen
10. *Blithe Spirit* by Noël Coward
11. Norman Mailer
12. Lyme Regis
13. Nine years old
14. Edna O'Brien
15. *The Jewel in the Crown*
16. Kenneth Grahame, *The Wind in the Willows*
17. *Portnoy's Complaint*
18. Anne Tyler
19. Majorca
20. *The Grapes of Wrath*
21. e e cummings
22. *Breakfast At Tiffany's*
23. Alan Ayckbourn
24. *Tender is the Night*
25. *Ulysses* by James Joyce
26. *The Camomile Lawn*
27. Erica Jong
28. Adrian Henri, Roger McGough or Brian Patten
29. *Sophie's Choice*
30. Vita Sackville-West

Quiz 61

Knowall's answer:
Paul McGann
1. Hugo Gernsback
2. Terry Pratchett's
3. Buck Rogers
4. The robot
5. An atomic holocaust
6. *The Day of the Triffids*
7. Godzilla
8. 42

ANSWERS

9. J. G. Ballard
10. Brian Aldiss
11. *A Clockwork Orange*
12. Arnold Schwarzenegger
13. Big Brother
14. *2010*
15. Orson Welles
16. Ripley
17. *Brave New World*
18. Edgar Rice Burroughs
19. Terry Gilliam
20. Witnessing the Allied bombing of Dresden
21. Isaac Asimov
22. *The Tempest*
23. His own death
24. Philip K. Dick
25. Michael Moorcock
26. "The Golden Age"
27. *The Terminator*
28. Alfred Bester
29. Room 101
30. Robert A. Heinlein

Quiz 62

Knowall's answer: Catherine Cookson's
1. Nigel West
2. Jeffrey Archer
3. Edwina Currie
4. *Watership Down*
5. *Icon*
6. Stephen King
7. Michelin
8. John Galsworthy
9. Bill Bryson
10. Ruth Rendell
11. Leslie Thomas
12. Jackie Collins
13. G. Macdonald Fraser
14. Jilly Cooper
15. Tom Clancy
16. Former royal jockey

Dick Francis
17. *The Lord of the Rings*
18. Tom Sharpe
19. *Pears Cyclopedia*
20. Sister Wendy Beckett
21. Ben Elton's
22. Thomas Hardy
23. Patricia Cornwell
24. Wilbur Smith
25. Graham Greene
26. The Golden Dagger
27. Oxford
28. Barbara Taylor Bradford
29. *Wisden*
30. David Cornwell

Quiz 63

Knowall's answer: "The wild beasts"
1. Andy Warhol
2. Salvador Dali
3. St Ives
4. Modigliani
5. Cubism
6. Henry Moore
7. The Tate Gallery
8. Willem de Kooning
9. Annigoni

10. Norwegian
11. Mondrian
12. David Hockney
13. Collage
14. Giacometti
15. Lucien Freud
16. John Piper
17. Kandinsky
18. Jacob Epstein
19. Paul Klee
20. Samuel Courtauld
21. Jackson Pollock
22. Andy Goldsworthy
23. Grandma Moses
24. Stanley Spencer
25. Marc Chagall
26. *Portrait of Dr Gachet* by Vincent van Gogh
27. Duncan Grant and Vanessa Bell
28. Leonardo da Vinci's *Mona Lisa*
29. Henri Matisse
30. Diego Rivera

Quiz 64

Knowall's answer: Manchester
1. L. S. Lowry
2. Joán Miró
3. Georgia O'Keefe
4. William Burrell
5. Augustus John (sister Gwen)
6. Maurice Utrillo
7. *Art Nouveau*
8. Barbara Hepworth
9. Switzerland (Zurich)
10. Graham Sutherland's
11. Pablo Picasso
12. Paul Cézanne
13. Roy Lichtenstein
14. Francis Bacon

15. Kinetic art
16. Jasper Johns
17. Claude Monet
18. Chief Crazy Horse in South Dakota, USA
19. Prince Charles
20. Damien Hirst
21. Austrian
22. The inside of a small house
23. René Magritte
24. Film making
25. The Pompidou Centre
26. Mabel Lucie Attwell
27. Anthony Blunt
28. Gerald Scarfe
29. Jean-Paul Getty
30. Henri Rousseau

Quiz 65

Knowall's answer: Kuala Lumpur, Malaysia (the twin Petronas Towers)
1. The Louvre, Paris
2. The Royal Festival Hall, London
3. Albert Einstein
4. Le Corbusier
5. Charles Rennie Mackintosh
6. Sir Norman Foster
7. The skyscraper
8. Sydney Opera House
9. Christo (Javacheff)
10. Bauhaus
11. The University of East Anglia, Norwich
12. The Sainsbury Wing
13. Sir Giles Gilbert Scott
14. The CN Tower
15. Otto Wagner
16. The Guggenheim Museum of Art

17. The Crystal Palace, Sydenham
18. Antonio Gaudi
19. In London's National Theatre complex
20. The Pompidou Centre
21. Brasilia
22. Russia
23. Coventry
24. Prince Charles
25. De Stijl
26. The Post Office Tower
27. Centre Point
28. The Chrysler Building
29. The Grand Coulee Dam
30. The Mound Stand

Quiz 66

Knowall's answer: The world's narrowest street at 17 inches (43 cm) wide
1. Chris Evert
2. 14
3. Castling (moving king and castle)
4. Boxing (a training demonstration)
5. Herbert Walker
6. 46
7. Spurs (2) v Chelsea (1)
8. Eight
9. The coypu
10. Iran, Iraq, Syria and Turkey
11. *Eleanor Rigby*
12. Sherpa Tenzing
13. Arthur Scargill
14. Actor Dennis Hopper
15. Silver
16. Abraham Lincoln and Andrew Johnson
17. England's longest place name

18. Juan Fangio (at 46)
19. Kashmir
20. A baseball bat
21. He said you can't see the Great Wall of China from the Moon
22. Nashville, Tennessee
23. 370 million
24. A shire horse
25. New Zealand
26. An analogue watch
27. Elizabeth Taylor
28. 39
29. In BBC shipping forecasts
30. 24,000

Quiz 67

Knowall's answer: Winnie-the-Pooh
1. Sutherland, Scotland
2. The Suez Canal
3. Boris Yeltsin
4. Strawweight
5. 1928
6. Anthony Booth
7. Mike Hawthorn (1958)
8. The "Empire Stadium"
9. Lionel "Buster" Crabbe
10. 42
11. Lester Piggott
12. 37 (0-36)
13. The King David Hotel
14. Franklin D. Roosevelt
15. Cruft's
16. 2nd Street
17. Ramsay MacDonald
18. Douglas Fairbanks Jnr
19. Lancashire (twice, 1990 and 1996)
20. The National Health Service (NHS)
21. Stefan Edberg

22. 3,000 feet (914 m)
23. Crown Prince Hussein
24. The Netherlands
25. Carp fishing
26. First live TV broadcast to Britain from overseas
27. *The Professionals*
28. 17
29. The *Bismarck*
30. Denis Compton

Quiz 68

Knowall's answer:
Ironbridge
1. Theodore Roosevelt and Woodrow Wilson
2. Egypt
3. Rocky Marciano
4. 1922
5. It was the last steam locomotive built for British Railways
6. Peru
7. Notting Hill
8. Katharine Hepburn (4)
9. The use of "canned" laughter
10. 1951
11. Shrove Tuesday
12. Majority verdicts
13. The European Common Market
14. Garfield Sobers (West Indies)
15. 9 million
16. John Grey Gorton
17. The Flying Squad
18. They were PE teachers
19. The "spoon"
20. That they could only serve for two terms
21. 71%
22. Julia Roberts

23. Moorgate
24. "The Prague Spring"
25. Indiana Jones
26. *Marionette* and *puppet*
27. Finland
28. 35
29. The *Olympic*
30. A bloodhound

Quiz 69

Knowall's answer:
Jimmy Nail
1. Suzanne Charlton
2. Betty (Michele Dotrice)
3. *The Crystal Maze*
4. Dickie Davies
5. *The A-Team*
6. Sean Bean
7. *The Upper Hand*
8. Ringo Starr
9. Gary Ewing (Ted Shackleford)
10. Mandy's husband, Trevor
11. *Flipper*
12. Connor
13. The *Crossroads* motel
14. Read the news
15. Jeremy Paxman
16. Barcelona

ANSWERS

17. *Fame*
18. *Billy Bunter of Greyfriars School*
19. Princess Anne
20. One (Lister)
21. *Are You Being Served?*
22. *Ready, Steady, Go!*
23. Terry Gilliam
24. Clive Anderson
25. Heineken
26. *Drop the Dead Donkey*
27. A Mini
28. Dennis Waterman
29. Boston
30. The Woolpack

Quiz 70

Knowall's answer: *Give us a Clue*
1. Jess
2. Carla Lane
3. A barber's shop
4. The National Indoor Arena, Birmingham
5. *Cool for Cats* (1956-61)
6. Noel Edmonds
7. As *The Fugitive*
8. Mobile Army Surgical Hospital
9. Rick, Neil, Vyvyan and Mike
10. Mutley
11. Michael Palin
12. Beverly Hills (*Beverly Hills 90210*)
13. Robin Day
14. *The Gentle Touch*
15. *Newsround*
16. Because his initials are ST
17. John Bird and John Fortune
18. Glasgow

19. Eamonn Andrews and Michael Aspel
20. Barney Rubble
21. Barfield Prison
22. Rising damp in *Rising Damp*
23. Anthony Aloysius Hancock (and Sid)
24. Sam Neill
25. *The Bill*
26. David Wicks
27. Leslie Nielsen
28. Hawaii
29. Vince (Paul Nicholas) and Penny (Jan Francis)
30. Trotter's Independent Trading

Quiz 71

Knowall's answer: Hercules
1. Saffron
2. *NYPD Blue*
3. Jim Bowen
4. Lee Chapman
5. A field of poppies
6. Raymond Burr
7. *The Mary Whitehouse Experience*
8. Bristol
9. Jools Holland
10. Francis Urquhart
11. *The Last of the Summer Wine*
12. Roald Dahl's
13. Theo Kojak's
14. Anne Haddy (Helen Daniels)
15. Parker
16. *Rough Guide*
17. Los Angeles
18. Granville is Arkwright's nephew

19. Richie Richard (Rik Mayall) and Eddie Hitler (Adrian Edmondson)
20. *Grange Hill*
21. 1955
22. Oprah Winfrey
23. Glenda Jackson
24. *Juke Box Jury*
25. Patrick Stewart
26. Kenneth Wolstenholme ("They think it's all over – it is now")
27. *Countdown*
28. Terry Wogan
29. *The Prisoner*
30. Jon Pertwee

Quiz 72

Knowall's answer: Rudolph Valentino
1. R2 D2 (Artoo-Deetoo)
2. An artist
3. *Jaws 2*
4. *Carry on Columbus*
5. Billy the Kid
6. Joy Adamson
7. Jeanette MacDonald
8. Bernard Cribbins
9. Jesus

10. Beethoven
11. Norfolk
12. Anthony Perkins
13. *Sid and Nancy*
14. Earth
15. *Help!*
16. *Babe*
17. 16
18. A peach
19. Three
20. *When Harry Met Sally*
21. The sinking of the *Titanic*
22. *Heat*
23. As *The Ladykillers*
24. "A slide trombone"
25. A sheet of glass
26. Alan Ladd (in *Shane*)
27. Five
28. Eli Wallach
29. A ukelele
30. *Duelling Banjos*

Quiz 73

Knowall's answer: Marilyn Monroe
1. Eric Liddell
2. *Oh, What a Beautiful Morning*
3. Ants
4. John Lennon
5. Manhattan (*Manhattan* and *Manhattan Murder Mystery*)
6. Tara
7. Skiing
8. Charlie Parker
9. Dean Martin and Rick Nelson
10. *Honeymoon in Vegas*
11. *The Seven Year Itch*
12. *The Sorcerer's Apprentice*

13. *A River Runs Through It*
14. *North by Northwest*
15. *The Nightmare Before Christmas*
16. Two
17. Robbie
18. *The Fly*
19. Blue
20. Seven
21. *G. I. Blues*
22. Robert Shaw
23. Paramount
24. Grace Kelly
25. A prison
26. Baseball
27. Peter Cushing
28. A top hat
29. Fletcher Christian
30. *Gandhi*

Quiz 74

Knowall's answer: *Doctor at Sea*
1. *The Colour of Money*
2. Baked beans
3. *Macbeth*
4. *The Terminator*
5. One (*The Berkleys of Broadway*)
6. Elm Street

7. U2
8. *Seven Brides for Seven Brothers*
9. Grace Kelly
10. A funnel
11. *Cinderella*
12. 23 years
13. *The Benny Goodman Story*
14. 1984
15. *The Godfather*
16. Bruce
17. *Borsalino*
18. *The Taming of the Shrew*
19. The Dave Clark Five
20. As *The Witches of Eastwick*
21. *Nine*
22. John Huston
23. Nobody – it was instrumental
24. *High Society*
25. Burl Ives
26. Tommy Steele
27. *Scrooge*
28. Sandra Bullock
29. Diane Hall
30. David Bowie

Quiz 75

Knowall's answer: A sword
1. Harley-Davidson
2. Max von Sydow
3. Steve McQueen, James Coburn and Charles Bronson
4. *The Man Without a Face*
5. Doc
6. Trevor Howard
7. *My Darling Clementine*
8. All three
9. Glen Campbell

10. Jimi Hendrix
11. George C. Scott
12. Elton John
13. Brigitte Bardot
14. Paul Newman
15. Tiberius
16. Jason Robards
17. Michael Caine
18. Mia Farrow
19. Three
20. Glenda Jackson (in *Women in Love*)
21. *Apocalypse Now*
22. Frank Sinatra
23. Pumbaa
24. Florida
25. Arnold Schwarzenegger
26. Rex Harrison
27. Julie Andrews
28. Dirk Bogarde
29. Stephen Sondheim
30. *Midnight Cowboy*

Quiz 76

Knowall's answer: Samuel Goldfish
1. Lee Marvin (1965)
2. A car
3. *Woodstock*
4. James Ivory and Ismail Merchant
5. His uncle
6. Tom Cruise
7. Bill Haley
8. Gustav Mahler's
9. Anthony Quinn
10. Bob Dylan
11. Miss Jane Marple
12. Barbra Streisand
13. Cecil B. DeMille
14. Sean Connery
15. David Puttnam
16. "Gabby"

17. *The Godfather Part II*
18. *Green Card*
19. Greta Garbo
20. Vests
21. Raquel Welch
22. W. C. Fields
23. Jane Russell
24. Robin Williams
25. *Rooster Cogburn*
26. Clinton Eastwood
27. *Peter Pan*
28. Mel Gibson
29. Michael Winner
30. The Searchers

Quiz 77

Knowall's answer: Muhammad Ali played himself
1. Arthur Miller (for Marilyn Monroe)
2. Val Kilmer
3. A skunk
4. *Oliver!*
5. A reel of film
6. Lenny Bruce
7. Bill and Ted
8. Aretha Franklin
9. "Popeye" Doyle
10. *A Shot in the Dark*
11. Mr Grimsdale
12. Marianne Faithfull
13. Jodie Foster
14. A tequila sunrise
15. William Hartnell
16. Soccer
17. *Gone with the Wind*
18. Whoopi Goldberg
19. Sydney Greenstreet
20. Steve Martin
21. Joan Crawford
22. *Monty Python and the Holy Grail*

ANSWERS

23. Anthony Hopkins
24. Cole Porter
25. Jayne Mansfield
26. François Truffaut
27. Jane Asher
28. Cannon and Ball
29. Gort
30. Jessica Lange

Quiz 78

**Knowall's answer:
Mike Todd**
1. Twiggy
2. W. C. Fields
3. Jane Seymour
4. The Big Bopper
5. Judy Garland and Mickey Rooney
6. MacLaine
7. Del Shannon
8. Charles Bronson
9. Estevez
10. Bob Dylan
11. Kirk Douglas
12. Jasper Carrott
13. Anne Bancroft
14. Lucille Ball
15. Michael Crawford
16. Elvis Costello
17. Brigitte Bardot

18. Eric Morecombe
19. Adam Faith
20. Nina Simone
21. George Burns
22. Johnny Rotten (of the Sex Pistols)
23. Cliff Richard
24. Yul Brynner
25. Stewart Granger (James Stewart)
26. Alvin Stardust
27. Stan Laurel
28. P. J. Proby
29. Michael Caine (*The Caine Mutiny*)
30. Marlene Dietrich

Quiz 79

**Knowall's answer:
Barry Manilow**
1. Barbra Streisand
2. Mantovani's
3. David Soul (Hutch of *Starsky and Hutch*)
4. *Aspects of Love*
5. *Three Coins in the Fountain, Stranger in the Night, Something Stupid* (*My Way* made No. 5)
6. *Nessun Dorma*
7. George Shearing
8. *Unchained Melody*
9. Eddie Calvert
10. Claude Debussy
11. Geoff Love
12. Elton John and George Michael
13. Bobby Darin
14. *Dragnet*
15. Tom Jones
16. *Big Spender*
17. Marvin Hamlisch

18. *Whatever Will Be Will Be*
19. Paul McCartney (with Wings – *Mull of Kintyre*)
20. Wolfgang Amadeus Mozart
21. *Misty*, by Johnny Mathis
22. Dionne Warwick
23. Tony Bennett
24. Elaine Paige
25. Enigma (*MCMXC AD* and *The Cross of Changes*)
26. Laverne
27. *Windmills of Your Mind*
28. *Tears*
29. Classical guitar
30. *The Life and Times of David Lloyd George*

Quiz 80

**Knowall's answer:
Peter Noone**
1. *Heartbreak Hotel*
2. Mick Fleetwood, Peter Green, Jeremy Spencer, John McVie (1967)
3. Don and Phil
4. *MacArthur Park*
5. Procul Harum (*Whiter Shade of Pale*)
6. *Love Letters*
7. The Spencer Davis Group
8. Beaky (in terms of weeks in the charts, the most successful group of 1966)
9. Decca
10. The Seekers (*The Carnival is Over* was No. 1)
11. Cliff Richard (*Move It*)

12. Brenda Lee
13. The Tremeloes (*Silence is Golden* was No. 1)
14. Bruce Channel's
15. Russ Conway
16. Al Martino
17. *Suzanne*
18. Peter Blake
19. Guy Mitchell and Tommy Steele
20. *Flowers In The Rain*
21. *Out Of Time*
22. Eddie Cochran
23. Julie Driscoll (with the Brian Auger Trinity)
24. Dean Martin
25. 1968
26. Mary Wilson
27. *Aftermath*
28. Bob Dylan
29. Jimi Hendrix (they were his drummer and bass guitarist)
30. *What Do You Want To Make Those Eyes At Me For?*

Quiz 81

Knowall's answer: The Stranglers
1. *Band of Gold*
2. Jasper Carrott
3. Malcolm McLaren
4. Bernie Taupin
5. Video
6. Don McLean (*American Pie*)
7. The flute
8. *Matchstalk Men and Matchstalk Cats and Dogs*
9. John Travolta and Olivia Newton-John

10. Donny (1971)
11. David Essex
12. Village People
13. In the sky
14. Alice Cooper
15. Rod Stewart
16. Led Zeppelin
17. Diana Ross
18. Electric Light Orchestra
19. The murder of students by a trigger-happy American student because she claimed "she didn't like Mondays"
20. T. Rex
21. Slade
22. Deep Purple
23. Black Sabbath
24. David Bowie
25. *Amazing Grace*
26. Abba
27. *Rivers of Babylon, Mary's Boy Child*
28. Desmond Dekker
29. Demis Roussos
30. Julie Covington

Quiz 82

Knowall's answer: Tom Jones'

1. *Careless Whisper*
2. Soft Cell's
3. *Peter Gunn*
4. Everything But The Girl
5. *In the Air Tonight*
6. *Imagine*
7. The Young Ones
8. Girls
9. Kim Wilde
10. *Orinoco Flow*
11. Shakin' Stevens
12. Simple Minds

13. *Stand and Deliver*
14. Al
15. *Rocky*
16. Bananarama
17. Phil Collins (the Live Aid concerts)
18. "Down the chip shop"
19. Bonnie Tyler
20. *The Power of Love*
21. Pet Shop Boys
22. *Making Your Mind Up*
23. Seattle
24. Kenny Everett
25. Bros
26. Jennifer Warnes (*Up Where We Belong, The Time of My Life*)
27. Martin Luther King
28. *Jealous Guy*
29. *Chariots of Fire*
30. *Beat It (No. 3)*: the rest were all No. 1s for Michael Jackson

Quiz 83

Knowall's answer: The three non-Gallagher members of Oasis

1. Eric Clapton
2. *Charly*
3. D:Ream
4. *Bring Your Daughter...To The Slaughter*
5. Kurt Cobain
6. David Geffen
7. *Music For The Jilted Generation*
8. *Dizzy*
9. Shakespears Sister
10. Shaggy
11. East 17 (*Stay Another Day*)
12. Hale and Pace (and the

Stonkers)
13. *Everybody Else Is Doing It, So Why Can't We?* (1993); *No Need To Argue* (1994)
14. Ireland
15. *Mmm Mmm Mmm Mmm* (Crash Test Dummies), *U* (Loni Clark)
16. *Robin Hood: Prince of Thieves*
17. *Robson and Jerome*, by Robson and Jerome, outsold *Unchained Melody*
18. *Parklife*
19. REM
20. Whigfield (*Saturday Night*)
21. New Kids on the Block
22. Prince (*The Most Beautiful Girl in the World*)
23. Salt-n-Pepa
24. Bruce Springsteen (*Streets of Philadelphia*)
25. Meatloaf
26. *Love Is All Around*
27. Blur (*Country House*)

28. Take That
29. *The Bodyguard*
30. Mariah Carey and Luther Vandross

Quiz 84

Knowall's answer: Bing Crosby

1. *Desert Island Discs*
2. Gary Powers
3. 32
4. Queen Mary (honorary degree, 1921)
5. Cigarette advertising
6. Somalia
7. Stavros Niarchos
8. Half-crown (2/6d, 12$^{1}/_{2}$p)
9. Laurence Olivier
10. *Independence Day*
11. Ted Willis
12. Virginia Wade
13. Meat (in 1954)
14. Bernadette Devlin
15. Naomi Campbell
16. Hugh Gaitskell
17. Gus Grissom, Ed White and Roger Chaffee
18. Pierce Brosnan
19. They committed mass suicide
20. Bo Derek
21. Kerry Packer
22. "Statto"
23. Bobby Moore
24. Copper
25. Valery Giscard d'Estaing
26. Keith "Cheggers" Chegwin
27. Eating flesh from dead bodies
28. Richard Branson

ANSWERS

29. *Children's Hour*
30. "Little Mo" (Maureen Connolly)

Quiz 85

Knowall's answer:
Aaron Spelling
1. Singapore
2. Leopold Stokowski
3. Both banned by the BBC
4. Vivienne Westwood
5. Three
6. A bel
7. Pasta
8. Nothing
9. Cannabis
10. Tim Rice
11. Genetic finger-printing
12. *Pennies From Heaven*
13. Pasadena
14. The Light Programme, the Third Programme and the Home Service
15. *Shaft*
16. 1935
17. Jim Morrison of the Doors
18. His son, Will Rogers Jnr
19. The grey squirrel
20. Refraction
21. Nice
22. Jacob Bronowski
23. Lincolnshire
24. Robert Maxwell
25. 1958
26. The Eager Beaver
27. The Gaza Strip
28. *Telly Addicts*
29. Orson Welles, who also starred and directed
30. Endeavour

Quiz 86

Knowall's answer:
Robert Runcie, former
Archbishop of Canterbury
1. Pancho Villa
2. Perennials
3. The hand
4. First trans-Pacific flight (San Francisco-Brisbane)
5. Carl Bosch
6. Pamela Anderson
7. President Richard Nixon
8. The Morris Minor
9. Trooping the Colour
10. Wayne Sleep
11. Smallpox
12. Daewoo
13. Alistair Cooke's
14. *Glasnost* and *perestroika*
15. Carol Drinkwater, Linda Bellingham
16. Dylan Thomas's
17. Teresa Gorman
18. Mainland
19. Sapper
20. The Windmill
21. Elspeth Huxley
22. Serendipity
23. Gregory's
24. Intel
25. Alfie Bass and Bill Fraser
26. Sri Lanka (then Ceylon)
27. The Volkswagen Beetle
28. The Photographer's Gallery (London), The Photographic Archive of the Bibliothéque Nationale (Paris)
29. *Gunsmoke, Gun Law*
30. Barrow-in-Furness

Quiz 87

Knowall's answer:
Runner-up Madge Syers
was a woman; she
subsequently won the
women's title three times
and Olympic gold for
Britain in 1908
1. Frank Woolley
2. The first man to win the Wimbledon and US Open titles in the same year
3. The Football League Championship
4. Yorkshire
5. Because he had been disqualified from winning the marathon after officials helped him across the line
6. They all won the Triple Crown (2,000 Guineas, Derby and St Leger)
7. Ice hockey (International Ice Hockey Federation)
8. Jack Hobbs
9. W. G. Grace
10. Billiards
11. To allow the Duke of Westminster time to return from New York; his powerful boat then hit a sandbank while well in the lead and did not finish
12. Tennis (Davis Cup)
13. The Intermediate Games (where medals were introduced)
14. Boxing was banned in the city (Corbett was a heavyweight, McCoy was a lightweight)
15. Berlin
16. Bernard Bosanquet (it was also called the "Bosie")
17. Tug-of-war
18. Steve Donoghue
19. Jess Willard
20. 1903
21. Alf Common (Sheffield United-Sunderland-Middlesbrough)
22. James Braid
23. Lottie Dod
24. Mercedes
25. Because most of the crowd were by then (well into World War 1) serving in the army
26. Billy Batten
27. Hazel Hotchkiss Wightman
28. C. B. Fry
29. Bob Fitzsimmons
30. Bury

Quiz 88

Knowall's answer: She
beat the men's record by
over two hours
1. Brooklands
2. Len Hutton
3. Fred Darling
4. Harold Abrahams

5. 1923
6. Alexander Obolensky
7. Derbyshire
8. Jesse Owens
9. The Jules Rimet Trophy
10. Bobby Jones
11. Betty Uber, whose name was later given to the world team championship
12. First man to reach 100mph (161km/h) on water
13. Paavo Nurmi
14. Swimming
15. The New York Yankees
16. Herbert Chapman
17. Kitty Godfree
18. Joe Davis
19. Andrew Sandham, 325 v West Indies
20. 1924
21. Jack "Kid" Berg
22. Water skiing
23. Sonja Henie (Norway)
24. Douglas Jardine
25. "Babe" Didrikson (Mildred Zacharias): she also won high jump

silver in 1932 and was renowned at billiards, diving and lacrosse
26. Scotland
27. Ryder Cup
28. Stanley Matthews
29. Alfred "Tich" Freeman (Kent)
30. Helen Wills-Moody

Quiz 89

Knowall's answer: Pat Taaffe
1. Eric Hollies
2. Chris Brasher, Chris Chataway
3. John Landy
4. Walter Donaldson
5. Judy Grinham
6. The first black players to make it in senior football and major league baseball
7. Les Jackson
8. John Charles
9. Ben Hogan
10. Arsenal
11. 1951
12. Joe Louis
13. The first "grand slam" (all four major open titles in the same year)
14. Torino
15. Lindrick
16. First six winners of the BBC Sports Personality of the Year, 1954-59
17. Dewi Bebb
18. The hang glider
19. Argentinian
20. Ken Scotland
21. Jeanette Altwegg
22. Australia

23. The Lonsdale belts (he was the 5th Earl of Lonsdale)
24. The New York Yankees
25. Ronnie Moore (1954, 1959), Barry Briggs (1957, 1958)
26. Surrey
27. Peter Collins
28. Peter Alliss
29. Devon Loch
30. American football

Quiz 90

Knowall's answer: Tony Nash (in the two-man bobsleigh)
1. Jim Alder
2. Mister Softee
3. Cam Nancarrow (Australia)
4. Tokyo
5. Louis Martin
6. Rod Laver
7. Colin Milburn (1969)
8. Jim Clark, Graham Hill
9. 1961, 1962
10. Table tennis
11. John Reid
12. Mike Hailwood
13. Basil d'Oliviera
14. Ron Hill
15. 1968
16. David Bryant
17. Pat Moss (Moss-Carlsson)
18. Gary Sobers: the feat was emulated by Ravi Shastri (Bombay) in 1985
19. Lillian Board
20. Fencing, in the modern pentathlon

21. Eddy Merckx
22. Mary Peters
23. The Badminton Horse Trials
24. Geoff Capes
25. Rugby union
26. Because of participant New Zealand's continued sporting links with South Africa
27. Leighton Rees
28. Renaldo Nehemiah
29. Tony Greig
30. Weightlifting

Quiz 91

Knowall's answer: Luxembourg
1. Karteem Abdul-Jabbar (formerly Lew Alcindor)
2. Jocky Wilson
3. American
4. Peter Scudamore
5. Steve Cram
6. Gina Campbell in *Agfa Bluebird II*: 198km/h (123mph)
7. Steffi Graf
8. Allan Wells (Scotland) & Mike McFarlane (England), both given 20.43 sec
9. Paul Ringer
10. Lennox Lewis
11. Viv Richards
12. Neil Adams
13. Fred Couples
14. Andrew Holmes (1988)
15. Essex
16. Sarajevo (1984 Olympics ice dancing)
17. Wigan
18. Jordan

ANSWERS

19. John Jeffrey
20. Jurgen Hingsen
21. England
22. Fatima Whitbread
23. Greg LeMond
24. 1983
25. Devon Malcolm
26. Lausanne
27. Colin Montgomerie
28. Va'aiga Tuigamala
29. Willie Carson
30. David Boon

Quiz 92

**Knowall's answer:
"Whispering" Ted Lowe**
1. Ben Johnson, shortly before the world indoor championships in Toronto, Canada – where he was found positive (again) and banned for life
2. The inimitable Murray Walker
3. Ilie Nastase
4. Brian Johnston
5. Steve Davis
6. John Sillett (Coventry City)
7. Barry McGuigan (with apologies to Mae West)
8. Noël Coward
9. Ian Baker-Finch (1991)
10. Ron Atkinson
11. Ian Chappell
12. Mickey Duff
13. Alex Murphy
14. Ray Illingworth
15. John Snagge (1952 Boat Race)
16. Victoria Wood (1989)
17. William Woollard

18. Stirling Moss
19. Bobby Robson
20. Rachael Heyhoe-Flint
21. His partner Tony Allcock
22. Canadian Bill Werbeniuk
23. Alan Minter
24. Jeff Thomson
25. Martina Navratilova
26. Idi Amin (he won the title in 1951)
27. George Best
28. Robin Williams
29. David Coleman (we had to have one)
30. Yes, our old friend Ted Lowe

Quiz 93

**Knowall's answer:
Graham Taylor**
1. Joe Fagan
2. Great Britain
3. Young Boys Berne
4. John Greig
5. Ruud Gullit
6. Leicester City (1961, 1963, 1969)
7. Martin Peters
8. First Division Falkirk
9. Pope John Paul II
10. Miguel Nadal
11. Stanley Matthews
12. Japan, South Korea
13. Billy Bremner
14. Moscow Dynamo
15. 108, 106 and 105
16. French
17. 7-1 (to Hungary)
18. Newcastle United
19. Bobby Charlton
20. Rotherham United

21. 1991-92
22. Ian Rush (Liverpool)
23. USA in 1994
24. Atlético Madrid: European Cup winners Bayern declined to take part
25. Hearts
26. Jimmy Delaney: Celtic 1937, Manchester United 1948, Derry City 1954 (he also won a runners-up medal with Cork Athletic in the FAI Cup in 1956)
27. Steaua Bucharest
28. 7-0
29. South Africa
30. Birmingham City

Quiz 94

Knowall's answer: Pickles
1. Peter Beardsley
2. Linfield
3. Netherlands (Holland)
4. Steve Claridge
5. David Platt (Aston Villa-Bari-Juventus-Sampdoria-Arsenal)

6. 1958: Wales lost 1-0 to Brazil, Northern Ireland 4-0 to France
7. Queen's Park Rangers
8. George Weah, AC Milan's Liberian (Eusebio, in 1965, was a naturalised Portuguese citizen)
9. Tony Hateley (Rangers' English striker)
10. (Stade de) Reims
11. Wolverhampton Wanderers (the figure is higher than for six Premier League clubs)
12. Patrick Kluivert
13. Stevenage Borough
14. Denis Law: he scored all City's goals in a 6-2 win abandoned with 21 minutes left – and Luton won the replay (despite another from Law)
15. Gremio Porto Alegre (Brazil)
16. Peter Shilton
17. Centre-back Bobby Moncur
18. Joe Mercer, caretaker England manager between Alf Ramsey and Don Revie in 1974
19. AC Milan
20. Rovers
21. Larry Gaetjens
22. Johan Cruyff, Michel Platini, Marco Van Basten
23. Arsenal in 1933 to 1935
24. Bobby Brown
25. Tottenham Hotspur in

the European Cup
Winners Cup
26. John Aldridge
(Tranmere, 27)
27. Bolton Wanderers to
Arsenal
28. Daniel Amokachi
(Everton), Efan Ekoku
(Wimbledon)
29. 1958
30. Gareth Southgate
(England's penalty
takers against Germany
in Euro '96)

Quiz 95

**Knowall's answer: In
Ohio, 44 years later, she
was killed during an
attempted robbery – and
the autopsy revealed
"she" was a man!**
1. *Running Brave*
2. Yachting
3. Valeriy Borzov
4. Diving (springboard)
5. *Supercalifragilistich-
expialidocious*
6. Vladimir Kuts
7. Coxed fours
8. Britons who won the
400 metres hurdles
9. 1964
10. It was the first gold
medal won by a woman
in competition with men
11. Lillehammer
12. 4th
13. It was the first time
women had run the race
in the Olympics
14. Matt Busby
15. Herb Elliott

16. Spain
17. Lasse Viren (Finland)
18. Paris (1900, 1924),
London (1908, 1948),
Los Angeles (1932,
1984)
19. Mary Decker (later
Slaney)
20. Italy (he won the
individual gold in
Rome in 1960)
21. Beijing
22. 13th
23. Munich, 1972
24. George Foreman
25. Jesse Owens
26. He set a record (still
standing) as the
Olympics' oldest gold
medallist at 64
27. Sapporo
28. 400 (they took four
months to complete)
29. Whatizit
30. Marie-Jose Perec

Quiz 96

**Knowall's answer:
Francis**
1. Fred Trueman

2. Nigel Benn
3. Alan Shearer
4. The 3,000 metres
steeplechase
5. Barry Sheene
6. Denise Lewis
7. Gordon Richards (269)
8. Virginia Wade, 1977
9. Steve Backley
10. Jayne Torvill and
Christopher Dean
(1981-84)
11. Kevin Keegan (1979)
12. Chris Finnegan
(middleweight) at
Mexico City in 1968
13. Ian Woosnam
14. Daley Thompson
15. Colin MacRae
16. Sally Gunnell
17. Stirling Moss: he never
won the World Drivers'
Championship (second
four times)
18. West Germany
19. Bob Willis
20. Garry Herbert, cox of
the gold medal coxed
pairs team
21. Russia's Yevgeny
Kafelnikov
22. John Hampshire
23. The Rugby League
Challenge Cup final at
Wembley
24. Mary Rand and Lynn
Davies (long jump)
25. Gareth Edwards
26. Neil Broad
27. Len Hutton
28. Robin Cousins
29. Rory Underwood
30. Jack Nicklaus

Quiz 97

**Knowall's answer:
The New Orleans Saints**
1. The Miami Dolphins
2. The Boston Red Sox
and the Pittsburgh
Pirates (5-3)
3. Michael Johnson (1996)
4. Chicago
5. Emmitt Smith
6. Payne Stewart
7. The Heisman Trophy
8. Mike Tyson
9. The Montreal Canadiens
10. The Kentucky Derby
11. The draft (picking
college players in turn)
12. Indycar racing
13. Hank Aaron of
Milwaukee and Atlanta
14. Joe Montana
15. He was the tallest player
in the NBA
16. Cycling
17. National Association for
Stock Car Auto Racing
18. He was pictured on a
cigarette card
19. Oakland
20. Dan O'Brien
21. Magic Johnson
22. Lou Gehrig
23. The San Diego Chargers
24. One
25. Chris Woods
26. Ice skating
27. The New York marathon
28. "The Eagles"
29. The forward pass was
legalised
30. Atlantic, Central,
Midwest and Pacific

ANSWERS

Knowall's answer: The compiler of the *London A-Z*, who traipsed 3,000 miles researching the capital's roads in the 1930s

1. Hubert Humphrey
2. 1974
3. Greta Garbo
4. *Voodoo Lounge*
5. Reliant
6. Harry Lime
7. The Dalai Lama
8. Somerset
9. John (23)
10. W. H. Smith
11. 1956
12. The Cartwrights
13. Tunisia
14. Henry Cooper, Joe Bugner, Richard Dunn, Brian London
15. 1971
16. The *Sea Empress*
17. Hilda Ogden (Jean Alexander) from *Coronation Street*
18. Leon Trotsky
19. Elaine Paige
20. Britain's withdrawal from the European Exchange Rate Mechanism (ERM)
21. Todd Woodbridge and Mark Woodforde
22. Peter Hall
23. "Deep Throat"
24. They were all prefaced by *"The Return of...."*
25. The Glums
26. 9 days
27. Bolivia and Paraguay
28. Grace Brothers
29. Alan Freed
30. 1982

Quiz 99

Knowall's answer: Thin

1. Lincoln
2. Conspicuous Gallantry Cross
3. *Thriller, Bad*
4. Esholt
5. Lacrosse
6. Shelley Winters
7. *The Black Bird*
8. Mark Ryland
9. El Cordobes
10. Bob Holness
11. David Byrne (Talking Heads; he objected to their using the name The Heads)
12. Groucho
13. *Life*
14. Hong Kong
15. Cinzano
16. "The Desert Rats"
17. John Wayne
18. A "Platinum Anniversary"
19. Influenza
20. Russell Harty
21. 1949
22. Lord Snowdon
23. W. G. Grace
24. Fastest transatlantic crossing by a passenger vessel (3 days, 7 hours, 52 minutes)
25. *Tribune*
26. Dawn Penn's
27. Canada
28. New York
29. 1989
30. *Barbarella*

Quiz 100

Knowall's answer: Sir Arthur Bliss

1. *Hair*
2. Brussels
3. Kenneth Williams
4. Meccano
5. Oder, Neisse
6. John Pilger
7. A buggy which uses satellite dishes to relay advice on fairway shots
8. Member of the American Society of Cinematographers
9. Timmy
10. Domestic science
11. Poland
12. *The Wizard of Oz* (1939), Judy Garland
13. The Green Party
14. Primo Carnera
15. 1969
16. Captain Mainwaring
17. Because children as young as 10 were working there
18. From the owners: actor-bandleader Desi Arnaz and wife Lucille Ball
19. Prince William of Gloucester
20. It was the number of films he reckoned he had previously made
21. Orinoco
22. 35
23. Somalia (on the equator from west to east)
24. The Winchester Club
25. 7 December 1941 – the Japanese attack on Pearl Harbor
26. Mel Blanc
27. Cambodia
28. 1980
29. Arizona (Oklahoma has the largest Native Indian population)
30. They were born on the same day: 3 April 1924.